This Storybook Belongs To

Princess _____

Sleeping Beauty

Once upon a time, in a faraway land, there lived King Stefan and his queen who held a great feast to celebrate the birth of their daughter, Aurora.

King Hubert of a nearby kingdom and his young son, Phillip, were guests at the feast. The two kings made plans for Prince Phillip and Princess Aurora to marry on Aurora's sixteenth birthday.

Three good fairies, Flora, Fauna, and Merryweather, also attended the party. Each of them brought a special gift.

Flora gave the princess the gift of beauty. Fauna gave the princess the gift of song.

Finally, Merryweather approached the cradle. Before she could offer her gift, a loud boom of thunder announced the arrival of Maleficent, the wicked fairy. She was very angry that she had not been invited to the feast.

Maleficent looked down at the sleeping infant. "I also have a gift for you," she began. "Before the sun sets on your sixteenth birthday, you will prick your finger on the spindle of a spinning wheel and die!"

When Maleficent left, Merryweather tried to calm the terrified crowd. "I still have my gift for the princess," she reminded everyone.

Raising her magic wand, the good fairy whispered, "Not in death, but just in sleep, the fateful prophecy you will keep. And from this slumber, you shall wake, when true love's kiss the spell shall break."

King Stefan still worried about Aurora's safety. He ordered every spinning wheel in the kingdom to be destroyed.

Then, the good fairies came up with a plan. They told the king and queen that they would disguise themselves as peasants and raise the child deep in the forest. When the curse ended on Aurora's sixteenth birthday, they would all return to the castle.

The king and queen reluctantly agreed.

Flora, Fauna, and Merryweather gave Aurora a new name: Briar Rose. They took her far into the woods to live in a little cottage. There, the fairies put away their magic wands so that Maleficent would never find them or Aurora.

As the years passed, Maleficent and her henchmen kept searching for the princess, but she was never found.

Finally, the wicked fairy sent her pet raven out to search. "Oh, my pet," said Maleficent. "You are my last hope. Circle far and wide. Search for a maiden with hair of sunshine gold and lips red as a rose. Go, and do not fail me!"

On the morning of Briar Rose's sixteenth birthday, the good fairies sent her out to collect berries so they could prepare her birthday surprise.

After gathering the berries, Briar Rose rested in the glade. She sang about her wish to fall in love with a handsome prince. Her friends, the animals and birds, listened happily.

Meanwhile, Prince Phillip had been riding through the woods on his horse, Samson. Phillip heard the beautiful voice in the trees and took off to find the singer.

Samson galloped along and, as he jumped over a log, the prince was thrown into a pond. He set his wet clothes out to dry.

Moments later, without the prince seeing them, the animals brought a cape, hat, and boots to Briar Rose. They dressed up as her make-believe prince and danced with her.

Prince Phillip followed the voice and discovered the beautiful maiden. He and Briar Rose fell in love at first sight.

But when the prince asked her name, Briar Rose remembered that the fairies had told her never to talk to strangers. When it was time for Briar Rose to go, she invited him to visit her cottage that evening.

Meanwhile, the three fairies were having a difficult time with their party preparations. Fauna made a lopsided birthday cake. Flora and Merryweather had made a special dress for Briar Rose, but something about it just didn't look quite right.

The good fairies needed a touch of magic to help them. So they agreed to use their wands—just this once.

Before trying out their wands, the good fairies blocked every opening in the cottage. They had to stop any magic dust from escaping and revealing their secret hideaway. But someone forgot to block the chimney!

Maleficent's raven flew by just as some magic streamed out of the cottage chimney. At last, the raven had found the princess! He raced back to the Forbidden Mountains to tell Maleficent.

By the time Briar Rose returned to the cottage, the party was ready. She thanked Flora, Fauna, and Merryweather for the beautiful new dress and delicious cake. "This is the happiest day of my life," she said.

Then she told them about the handsome stranger she had met in the woods. "I invited him to come here this evening," she explained.

The fairies realized that Briar Rose had fallen in love. "It's time we told her the truth," said Fauna sadly.

Briar Rose learned that she was really a princess who was betrothed to a prince named Phillip. "I'm sorry, child," said Flora. "Tonight we're taking you back to your parents, the king and queen."

As soon as darkness fell, the good fairies led a sad Briar Rose through the forest to the castle. As she walked, Briar Rose could only think of her handsome stranger.

At the castle, Flora, Fauna, and Merryweather left Aurora in a quiet room to rest. Suddenly, a strange glowing light appeared. Aurora followed it in a trance-like state. It led her up a winding staircase to an attic room. Inside the room was Maleficent—waiting by a spinning wheel.

Aurora reached out. She pricked her finger on the spindle and fell to the floor.

As soon as the good fairies discovered Aurora, they cast a spell over the kingdom, putting everyone to sleep. This would save the king and queen from heartbreak and give the good fairies time to find Aurora's true love. Only true love's kiss could break the spell.

Between snores, the fairies heard King Hubert mention something about his son, Prince Phillip, wanting to marry a peasant girl.

The fairies realized that Briar Rose's stranger must be the prince! They hurried back to the cottage to find him.

But they were too late. Maleficent had captured Prince Phillip and was keeping him prisoner in her dungeon.

The good fairies went to Maleficent's dungeon and freed the prince. Then they gave him the magical Shield of Virtue and the Sword of Truth.

Prince Phillip used the sword to cut his way through a forest of thorns.
There, he came upon Maleficent who had turned herself into a fierce and terrible
dragon. But the dragon was no match for Phillip and the Sword of Truth.

After slaying the dragon, Phillip raced back to the castle and found Aurora. Kneeling down beside her, he kissed her gently. The princess awakened with a smile.

Flying about, the good fairies woke up everyone in the kingdom. And that night, the prince and his princess danced happily in each other's arms.

THE **SULLIVAN STREET**
BAKERY COOKBOOK

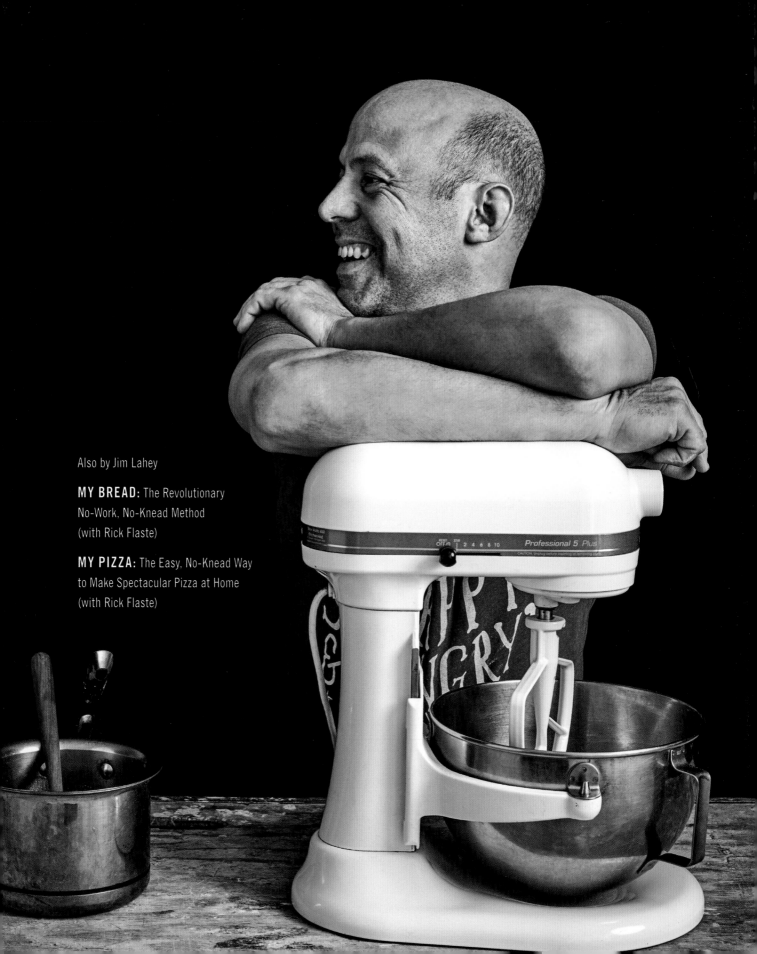

Also by Jim Lahey

MY BREAD: The Revolutionary
No-Work, No-Knead Method
(with Rick Flaste)

MY PIZZA: The Easy, No-Knead Way
to Make Spectacular Pizza at Home
(with Rick Flaste)

THE SULLIVAN STREET BAKERY COOKBOOK

JIM LAHEY

WITH **MAYA JOSEPH**

PHOTOGRAPHY BY **SQUIRE FOX**

W. W. NORTON & COMPANY

INDEPENDENT PUBLISHERS SINCE 1923

NEW YORK | LONDON

For information about permission to reproduce selections from this book,
write to Permissions, W. W. Norton & Company, Inc.,
500 Fifth Avenue, New York, NY 10110

For information about special discounts for bulk purchases,
please contact W. W. Norton Special Sales at
specialsales@wwnorton.com or 800-233-4830

Manufacturing by RR Donnelley Shenzhen
Book design by Jan Derevjanik
Production manager: Anna Oler

ISBN 978-0-393-24728-2

W. W. Norton & Company, Inc.
500 Fifth Avenue, New York, N.Y. 10110
www.wwnorton.com

W. W. Norton & Company Ltd.
15 Carlisle Street, London W1D 3BS

1 2 3 4 5 6 7 8 9 0

TO DECLAN, ANJALI, AND PIA

Traditional panettone (page 225).
Naturally leavened, with citron and raisins.

CONTENTS

SULLIVAN STREET

SULLIVAN STREET IS ONE OF NEW YORK'S MORE BEGUILING STREETS. NAMED after a Revolutionary War general, it begins at the southwest end of Washington Square Park. From there it ambles south, enjoying a few blocks in the Village before skipping across Houston, gliding through the elegant blocks of SoHo, careening into the chaos of Sixth Avenue, and disappearing forever.

It is a short street. In the 1990s, it was calm and shady and shimmered in the embers of the Italian neighborhood it had once been. Pino's Prime Meats and Joe's Dairy and an old ravioli factory graced the street, along with a host of eagle-eyed Neapolitans who knew the genealogy of each inch of it and those who walked it. When my bakery opened—in 1994—my new neighbors were eager to tell me how back in *their* day the bakers on Sullivan Street made home deliveries, every day, rain or shine or sweltering heat, up sixth-floor walk-ups and beyond, carrying hot loaves of bread on wooden planks. (They also smiled at me gently, with a shake of the head, saying my bread was "*too dark*, Jimmy"—but some things never change).

The neighborhood was changing, though, giving way to expensive art galleries, vacant storefronts, and abandoned lofts. The old Italians who rarely left the neighborhood soon muddled with the swaggering young artists streaming in. It was an odd yet amiable collision, a peculiar tincture of old world meets art world. It felt like the perfect place to start my bakery.

The breads that I wanted to make were inspired by village bakeries in Italy, but crossed with my own whims and wiles. The Italian bread I had fallen in love with in the 1980s was magnificent, well-built, living bread. It was bread that may have been baked that day but was clearly descended from something that had been made and eaten since ancient times. It was big, imperfect, crusty bread. It was not meant for slicing. It was messy and rough and meant to be ripped and dipped and respected and treasured. Its forms eternal, its functions essential, it embodied thousands of years of agricultural traditions, baking practices, and table manners. I wanted to make bread like it: a dark crackling crust that split open to reveal a creamy white interior whose hot perfumes spilled out in a delirium of aromas. If my way would eventually come to differ from the practices I had learned in Italy, that was fine. I wanted not the method but the spirit of this bread, and if it was only imperfectly Italian, or Italian*ish*, then I would embrace that dusky territory. My bakery was like a workshop, filled with clouds of flour and gusts of wheat bran, where every available surface was a place to tinker and experiment and depart from some traditions while remaining faithful to others.

I was devoted and obsessed. I talked to anyone and everyone about the history of this bread, about its chemistry and viscosity and the grams of yeast I had used that morning and the ambient humidity of the day and the heat distribution of my steam-tube oven. Many thought I was crazy (really, though, have you ever met a baker who wasn't?). But my bread *was* beautiful, and I loved making it and enjoying the feeling of feeding this neighborhood.

Whenever I had time and was nostalgic for the smells and tastes of the bakeries I had loved in Italy, I would make a *crostata*—a quick crust spread with jam—or little sandwiches—or a *ciambella*—the simplest of cakes.

Soon Sullivan Street Bakery was home to a bustling crowd of blustering artists, wary Italians, and incredibly curious tourists. Like the aging mobster who coolly traversed the streets in his bathrobe, seeking—some whispered—to authenticate the insanity plea with which he had evaded prison, we had become a part of the neighborhood.

And then, thirteen years later, my business partnership broke up, and Sullivan Street Bakery moved!

I kept the name, of course—for the soul of the bakery will always be that of Sullivan Street, but now the bakery resides in Hell's Kitchen, with a branch in the New York neighborhood of Chelsea, and another in Miami. We make the same bread and now serve what I think of as "baker's food"—meals or snacks made to go with bread or cooked alongside bread, in the heat of the baker's oven. I am happy to report that my original neighbors sometimes make the trek up from SoHo to find us again.

The Sullivan Street of 1994 may have faded into the fuzzy realm of nostalgia, but its amiable personality of artsy quirkiness crossed with old-world integrity still aptly sums up our character and our mission.

Roman Bread, My Way

When I fell in love with Italian bread, it happened in Rome. I was twenty-one and there to study art. But I became obsessed with the bread. I made a practice of haunting Rome's bakeries. I am a contrarian by nature, so it only piqued my interest that the bakers of Rome unanimously lifted up their hands in impatience and told me to go away. "Eh! American!" they would say, "don't worry about this bread. Go see some *palazzi*!" But I was enthralled. Like the gods of ancient Rome, the breads and bakeries of this city were an old and ancient cosmos, full of relics and legends and odd characters. Visiting some bakeries was like stepping back in time by a few hundred . . . or thousand years. Conditions were primitive. The bakers were pretty weird. And the bread was unworldly. There was *pizza bianca alla romana*, for instance—a six foot long flat plank of bread which always gave me a distinct feeling of unease. (At first glance it looks altogether too much like a crocodile's back emerging from a river). But hot out of the oven and smelling piney and fragrant with fresh rosemary and olive oil, it was magnificent.

I soon fell into the habit of wandering Rome's markets, asking all the oldest-looking women: "*Scusi, ma Lei sa dove posso trovare il miglior pane a Roma? O un ottimo panificio? Per favore.*" Excuse me, but where can I find the best bread in Rome? Or the best bakery, please? And they would send me on a meandering journey to somewhere not quite the city and not quite the country.

Inevitably, I found a crumbling, dusty, ill-lit structure. Peering into the darkness would yield little to the eye: a miscellany of wooden objects. Boards, slats, crates, tools to load and unload the oven. They rhythmic sound of the wooden tools scuffling bread in and out of the oven mixed with the quiet noises of hot bread crackling. What were the secrets of these crumbling old bakeries?

The first thing I noticed about the best village bakeries in Italy was that they didn't make twenty things. They made one or two breads. Or they made one dough, and turned that single dough into a variety of different breads. These were not French bakeries with a rigorous and obsessive method. There *was* a method, but it was quiet and relaxed, based on practice, experience, and a determined grappling with what I think of as a particularly Italian quest: How to achieve sublime beauty with the least amount of effort.

Not only does using a single dough to make a range of breads make life easier for the baker, but I find that it also leads to better bread. Handling the same dough over and over and over again, mixing and cutting, shaping and baking it, and transforming it into a diversity of shapes and products yields a familiarity with how that dough behaves in a variety of conditions.

I follow this practice at Sullivan Street Bakery, where we sell many breads, but only mix a few different doughs. I credit the practice of making a few really exquisite doughs with sustaining both my sanity and the business. (Running a successful 24-hour-a-day, 365-days a year wholesale bakery in New York City is about as easy as you'd imagine.) I have replicated this approach in this cookbook—using just a few basic methods and types of dough to make a variety of breads and pizzas.

Cooking and Baking at Home

In my first cookbook, *My Bread*, I described how my no-knead, Dutch-oven cooking method (bread cooked in a heavy, heated pot in an extremely hot oven) allows you to make Sullivan Street–style breads at home. The oven-within-an-oven technique is a way to make a gorgeous, crusty loaf with about five minutes of work.

In this book I use the same technique but also share how to develop flavors *inside* the loaf using natural leavening and, at times, a pinch of baker's yeast. Natural leavening—also known as *sourdough*—is responsible for the divine aromas and textures in the Roman breads I long ago fell in love with. Its purpose in bread dough is not to sour it but to *leaven*, or raise it. It can take a few days to get the process up and running, but if you are looking for bread with incredible flavors and textures, it is well worth the extra steps.

Many bakers are acquainted with a liquid sourdough starter—a slurry of water and flour that is allowed to sour as it fills with beneficial microbes. I follow an older and easier method of making sourdough breads. I use "old," soured dough itself, rather than a liquid starter. A fermented piece of dough used to leaven a bigger piece of dough is often called a *pre-ferment*: I adopt the Italian word for a pre-ferment—*biga*—as the name for my particular type of doughy starter.

It has the same name and formula that I use in the bakery to make nearly all of our breads—such as the *Pane Pugliese* (page 76), whose dark, malty crust contrasts so marvelously with the creamy-colored, pillowy crumb within; the light, golden *Ciabatta* (page 85); or the nutty, seedy *Multigrani* (page 99).

The fragrant, airy crumb structure of the breads I bake requires wet, loose doughs. Even if you wanted to knead them, it would be inadvisable! The doughs can be so wet that "kneading" them by hand involves lifting them up into the air as high as you can and throwing them down to the counter with terrific force. (I have done this, and it is fun, but the mess is—even by my standards—incredible!) Rather than kneading (or throwing), many of the bread recipes in this book—such as the *Pane Bianco* (page 89) or *Truccio* (page 93)—rely on a long fermentation (at times 18–22 hours) and gently folding the dough over on itself a few times. It is easy, simple, and mess free.

I have found that other bread doughs—such as my *Pugliese* or Pizza Bianca (page 65 or 118)—lend themselves to being mixed in a stand mixer. They are still too silky and elastic for a dough hook, but they come together quite nicely with the open web of a pastry paddle (sometimes called a *flat beater*) attachment. Whenever this is an option, I give two ways to mix a dough—one method by hand and one faster method in a stand mixer.

I have included a few variations for some of the breads because discovering that the same basic dough can work in a bunch of different recipes is fun and, I hope, useful. So, if you enjoy making the No-Knead, Naturally Leavened Brioche (page 107), for instance, it is pretty cool to know that the same dough can be turned into Cardamom Cinnamon Buns (page 147), a

Chocolate Swirl Brioche Loaf (page 150), *Bomboloni* (Italian Doughnuts, page 153), or even little slider buns for a cookout (page 111).

I also share some of my favorite recipes for the breakfasts and lunches that we serve at the bakery. When it comes to cooking, I find that I always want just one or two ingredients to be the star of a dish. I want to make that ingredient really shine, to show it off, to add other items only to bring out the star's key elements. Seasonality and frugality are at roots of the kind of cooking I like.

The Italian term for this kind of food is *la cucina povera*—it is the art of cooking well with what's available. I think of it as imagining and making magnificent dishes out of seemingly commonplace ingredients.

Of course, I don't live in Italy—I live in New York, on top of my bakery. Everything I make I consider to have been influenced by Italy, but there is plenty that I make, both at home and in my bakery, that would never be found in Italy. I call my approach to cooking Italian-*ish*; and if I had to define it, it would be the practice of cooking in a way that makes one or two ingredients shine, using the foods and spices I find around me—whether lavender from the garden or pasilla chiles from the bodega down the street.

Many of the roasts and sandwiches and pizzas I feature here (such as the Chicken, Avocado, and Kimchi Sandwiches, page 185, or the Carrot Pizza with Clementines and Olives, page 127) thus stray a bit off the path of strict Italian traditions—but I consider them guided by my belief in bringing out a few key flavors in a dish, and I like to think that they would be as welcome on an Italian table as they are by my customers in New York.

The desserts—*dolci*—include a few innovations, like the *Caprino* (a goat cheese and rhubarb cookie, page 207) and *Colpa Degno* (a flourless triple-chocolate cookie, page 211) which slip easily into the lexicon of Italian baking, and my own favorite versions of traditional Italian desserts. I associate Italian desserts with comfort and simplicity—nothing fancy, only the welcoming smells of an anise-flavored cake (Ciambella, page 212) or the sight of a pretty tart baked with custard and pine nuts (*Pinolata*, page 220), or of course, a Crostata di Marmalata (page 216)—the rustic tart glistening with jam whose appearance on a table never fails to bring back memories of the mornings I spent baking for my neighbors on Sullivan Street.

Biga (page 51), ready to use.

2

BAKING WITH SOURDOUGH

A WALK IN THE WOODS IS LIKE A SOJOURN IN A FARAWAY LAND. FOR A BRIEF
time, we might surrender to the crunch of the forest floor, the discreet scurrying of deft, unseen feet, the *thwomp* of a large branch plummeting. It is a country independent of us. And yet its language is neither strange nor unwelcome. It is calming and often—for me at least—a sensory relief to slink in line with the trees, tread on soft moss, and smell the dampness of fallen logs.

There is a natural order to the woods. Baking with sourdough is, oddly enough, similar.

We tend to worry about technique in baking. Precision, mastery, perfection. Control. I like all of these things. But the reasons that I *enjoy* baking have more to do with tactile pleasure than textbook perfection. I like to observe. I watch dough. I smell it and taste it, poke at it and pull at it. If it's baking, I listen to it. I fix my thoughts on the senses that usually melt into the background. It is a kind of meditation. Almost like a walk in the woods.

Mixing

The nicest way to mix flour and water together is by hand. Swirl your hand through a bowl of flour and water to combine them. Do it at full force, with violence, even, so that it splatters. And then stop! If done fast enough, the flour and water will change from soup to cement in ten seconds or less. This is a good bread dough!

The tempest of activity ("*frusta!*" in Italian) fills the new dough with tiny air bubbles and brings the flour and water together. Mixing dough in this way is a kind of forced matchmaking. The flour and water, tossed together in the most brutal fashion, are left to find their own way to fit together.

As you scrape the dough off your fingers and drop it back into the bowl, you will notice it is loose. It is not yet a unit. Like wet scrambled eggs, the dough will be scraggly. It will not yet stick together.

Tidy people will want to tidy it and I will whisper in their ear, *please, let the dough be messy.* In the no-knead method, loose, messy dough is the ugly duckling of breads. Left to its own devices, it will become the soft and feathery heart of a beautiful bread.

Kneading

Kneading can be fun, but it is less fun when using the kind of wet doughs that I like to make. Wet doughs yield breads with pillowy interiors, which is why I like them. But wet doughs start out as a kind of soupy muddle, which is hard to knead.

I once read in a baking textbook that the only way to knead a wet dough by hand was to stand very high above a table and throw the dough down on it with as much force as possible. The baker was to scrape the dough off the table, and repeat the process until the dough was elastic and supple—about 45 minutes. I tried this method. I was left sweaty, exhausted, and in awe of the mess. It did work, but I did not make a habit of this method.

In a bakery, it is easy to knead wet doughs: we do it in a commercial mixer that has the power to spin 500 pounds of dough. At home, many people use a stand mixer with a bread hook in the same way, but this is not a good fit for a wet dough.

Dough hooks are designed for stiff doughs, and mixing a wet dough with a hook is like using a spoon to chop an onion. It may work, but only with a potential loss of sanity. (Or in this case, the motor of the stand mixer, which may expire in a fruitless quest to catch hold of the loose, slushy dough).

Sometimes I use the pastry paddle (or as some call it, the "flat beater") of my stand mixer to mix/knead a wet dough, and that often works well. The open webbing of the pastry paddle helps pull a wet dough of a certain consistency together. This is a helpful trick, for a stand mixer dough will always leaven faster than a no-knead dough. The intensive, high-speed mixing does the same thing as kneading: it conditions the dough and vastly speeds up the time it takes to develop and rise. Whenever it is possible to use this method in the recipes that follow, I describe it.

Sometimes I use this method myself, but mostly, when I bake Sullivan Street breads at home, I prefer to make them as "no-kneads." I mix them together quickly by hand (10 seconds or less), and then let them come together on their own. The strengthening and knitting together of the dough that happens with intensive kneading or mixing will also occur without kneading or other interventions, if enough time is allowed.

There is an exceptional beauty and mystery in watching the dough transform *itself* from an unlovely mess to a tidy, buoyant ball of energy.

Ballooning

When water comes in contact with wheat flour, there are two special proteins in the wheat that are inspired to action. Called glutenins and gliadins, they start moving at the first contact of water and flour. Throughout the new dough, they slip toward each other and combine. Their unions create a new protein—gluten. As gluten develops across the dough, it reaches out in every direction to form increasingly complex chains and webs.

Poke a finger into the dough after the initial ten seconds of mixing and it will meet a soupy

Pane bianco (page 89) in five stages, clockwise from the top left: just mixed, 20 minutes later, fully leavened and ready to shape, just shaped, fully proofed and ready to bake.

pudding. Twenty minutes later, there will be the slightest bit of tension where there was none before. This is the warp and woof of a newly made gluten network. At this point, I often recommend gently picking up the edges of the dough and folding them into the center, just like the folds on the back of an envelope. This simple action brings more areas of the dough in contact and allows gluten chains more occasions to unite and cross-link.

As the dough sits, the gluten networks will weave and unweave and reweave their laces to form stronger, finer webs. (This is why I implore readers, when mixing by hand, to stop mixing as soon as the dough has barely come together. Mixing, fussing, and tidying past the point at which flour meets water forces the developing gluten chains into what I think of as knots, which would only unravel with intensive kneading.)

After several hours, the dough will even out. It will look and feel tight. Pull a bit of the dough toward you and it will snap in two, like a rubber band stretched past its limits.

After several more hours, the dough will have a smooth, glassy sheen to it.

Given enough time, it will develop a celebrated and amazing kind of stretch called visco-elasticity. This sublime stretchiness allows dough to expand in any direction—and hold a shape at the same time.

The gluten matrix will become so microscopically sturdy that it can trap gas and expand with it—exactly like a balloon.

Eventually it will fill with small, balloon-like bubbles. As they rise upward they lift the dough. When there are enough bubbles, they make the dough wobble. A gentle jab into the dough's surface at this point will meet a giddy, jiggly resistance. Pulling bits of it up into the air will reveal stringy, viscous threads that will often stretch and separate in an infinity of webs—much like hot pizza cheese or well-chewed gum—before eventually snapping back toward the bowl and merging back into the dough.

While the proteins in the flour are preparing this fabric, the flour's starches are being cut into different kinds of sugars and digested. In a batch of conventional bread, the baker uses packaged yeast to digest, or "ferment" these sugars. In sourdough bread, the baker relies on wild yeast and bacteria to ferment the dough. In each case, starches are broken down into simple sugars and turned into alcohol and a common gas: carbon dioxide.

As the yeasts and bacteria do their work and multiply, fermentation speeds up and levels of carbon dioxide build up inside the bread. The tiny bubbles of air that were mixed into the dough in the initial ten-second scramble now fill with carbon dioxide. (If there were no ready-made bubbles, the carbon dioxide would dissipate into the dough).

By the time that fermentation has reached full throttle, the gluten webbing of the dough will also be reaching its peak.

Thanks to the stretchy lacework of the gluten networks, the growing bubbles of carbon dioxide rarely pop. They simply swell. As the dough fills with gas from fermentation, gluten holds the gas in, trapped inside delicate, expanding walls of amazing strength and stretchiness.

Natural Leavening

When a baker checks to see if the dough has "doubled" or "tripled" in size, they are really checking how gassy it is. By the time that it is ready to shape into a round or an oval or divide into rolls, the dough will be so full of gas bubbles that if you gently shake its container, it will bounce and quiver like a water balloon. A "gassy" dough is a sign of two things: well-developed gluten networks that can retain gas and energy, and a lot of fermentation.

An ordinary loaf of bread is leavened with packaged, commercial yeast. Whether "rapid rise," "instant," "compressed," or another form, it is all the same variety of *Saccharomyces cerevisiae*, a kind of brewing yeast. *S. cerevisiae* has been specially manufactured for the purpose of raising a loaf quickly and predictably. And it does! It is a reliable and wonderful substance. It has one drawback, though. It does not create much flavor. Using a tiny bit is inoffensive. Using it in large quantities for a presto-right-away loaf leads to flavors that I find rather soapy.

A loaf of sourdough bread is leavened with "natural leavening"—a collection of wild yeast and bacteria. They work together to ferment the dough in much the same manner as packaged yeast. But they do the work in stages (the yeast tend to start work first) and both the wild yeasts and the bacteria work at a more languorous pace than packaged yeast. They are worth indulging because they perform certain benedictions upon the dough along the way.

Natural leavening influences gluten development and changes the texture of the dough. The interior, or crumb, of a naturally leavened loaf can feel delicate but substantial, billowy and feathery and sturdy, in a way that an ordinary loaf never can.

And the bacterial aspect of natural leavening, in particular, releases a rarefied mix of flavoring compounds. These range from the buttery notes of lactic acid to the vinegary bite of acetic acid, and an exotic medley of esters, aldehydes, and ketones. Every climate and microclimate will produce its own unique assortment of wild yeast and bacteria, so the natural leavening of any particular place will vary. Sniffing the crumb and crust of a naturally fermented loaf of bread is a sport a bit like sampling the bouquet of a glass of wine. There is a stunning range of smells and flavors in a dough or loaf of well-made sourdough bread. Contrary to the name, though, actual sourness need not be one of them.

How Sour a Sourdough?

A naturally leavened dough that sits and ferments for a long time before it is baked can eventually become quite sour. In my opinion, that is not a desirable result. I bake with sourdough because I like the way that natural leavening reveals and enhances the flavors of the wheat, and perfumes the crust and crumb with its own enthralling scents. When a bread becomes too acidic, these milder flavors are overpowered. There are some people—such as aficionados of a classic San Francisco sourdough—who do enjoy a high degree of acidity, but for me, biting sourness only creeps into the dough by mistake.

When I smell or taste extreme acidity in a developing dough, I take it as a signal that the dough is *overfermented*. Fermentation has gone on so long that too much acid has built up in the dough. This has consequences beyond taste—an overfermented dough is also running out of energy, and will not be able to rise much more than it already has. In addition, when a dough becomes too acidic, the yeasts go on strike. A very sour dough is likely to become a dense bread.

There is one undeniably sour aspect to the sourdough process: the starter.

Flour and Water

We often feel the effects of the microscopic elements of the natural world without actually seeing the elements at work. It is so rare to even think about them it feels a little like a magic trick or comic book alchemy act to actually watch natural fermentation occur.

It is also a surprisingly easy process to harness. Wild yeasts and their bacterial partners in fermentation are on us and all around us. They are found on most plants and your flour is likely saturated with them. I usually have success in "starting" a starter by simply mixing flour and water together and waiting for the yeast to "wake up." This can take anywhere from 1 to 4 days. Here is what happens.

Yeasts are quicker to the draw than bacteria, and you will see their activity first: a few bubbles of carbon dioxide floating to the surface. As they ferment the flour and their numbers increase, you will see more and more bubbles. A deliciously yeasty, alcoholic vapor will hover over the mixture, and smell a bit like wine that has sat out overnight in a glass. As the bacteria wake up and also get to work, you will smell acids, and the pungent, sour tang of bacteria at work. Soon a whiff of the starter will bring to mind an unpleasant vinegar or slightly offensive cheese. Eventually bubbles of carbon dioxide will fill the jar and, as in a loaf of bread, they will push upward. In a starter, they will take some of the flour with them, creating a foamy raft of flour at the top of the water. At this point my own favorite starter often gives off a distinctive aroma of sulphur, like a healthy, just-peeled hard-boiled egg. Some people stir their starter constantly in the hopes of speeding up fermentation, but I never do, because I like to watch this process.

It is worth refreshing a starter (pour out all but a teaspoon and add fresh flour and water) a few times to become acquainted with its rhythms and also ensure it is healthy.

This process could take several days. (But if you wanted a quick and ordinary bread, you'd probably already have made it!)

What Goes Up Must Come Down

Whether in a starter or a bread dough, the bubbles of carbon dioxide will eventually deflate or pop. A starter will rise and then fall, and the flour will settle to the bottom of the mix. A bread dough will rise. If it is naturally leavened and sits around long enough, it will acidify and then deflate. Eventually it will even liquefy, just like a starter.

A starter is extremely unstable. Its rise and collapse happens with such (relative) speed that it needs to be fed new doses of flour quite often to keep it going.

Once I have a basic starter, I avoid this routine by giving my starter about one thousand times too much food.

I mix a spoonful of starter into a bowl of flour and a little water and come back in twelve hours, when this floury mix has changed into a well-aerated, yeasty-smelling sponge. It holds this state for another twelve hours or so and then it collapses into a thick, sticky, acidic dough. Once it rises, it is ready for bread making and, refrigerated, it stays ready for a week or (sometimes) more. Whether newly inflated or long-deflated, a knob of this "mother dough" will leaven a loaf. After the Italian word for "pre-ferment" (something added to a dough), I call this mixture a *biga*.

A biga is a valuable substance because it not only frees a baker from the regime of starter feedings but also is doughy enough that it follows the exact trajectory of a real loaf of bread. Watch a biga rise and fall a few times, and you will have a very good idea of the path that your bread dough is going to follow. (Except that you'll want to shape and bake your dough before it collapses).

Waiting

If baking with sourdough called for any particular skill, it would be knowing how long to wait. Fermentation is like an exponentially increasing explosion. It begins slowly. Added to dough, the yeasts and bacteria in a biga get to work right away, but their primary job is not fermentation: it is replication. As the yeasts and bacteria reproduce and multiply, fermentation speeds up. It goes faster and faster as the number of microbes swells. The same dough that did nothing for the first six hours may appear to buzz with uncontrollable activity twelve hours later.

Baking with sourdough does not follow a set schedule. It is predictable—you know what will eventually happen—you just do not know *exactly* how long it will take. A bread may have a suggested fermentation time of 6 to 8 hours, and could take far, far longer. This imprecision is one of the reasons I like it. I like the *act* of making bread, I like good bread, and I also like the fact that I am compelled to "turn off" my ordinary thoughts in order to find my way. It is not hard to watch the dough and give it a tug now and then, and a sniff here and there, but in our busy, digital modern era, it is an unusual way of relating to the world. I find it soothing and exciting. I hope that you do, too.

Whether you start with a starter, a biga, or a bread dough, you'll begin by mixing flour and water, and sinking into the rhythms and humming order of a busy, tiny, magnificent world.

INGREDIENTS

Flour

Every recipe in the book has been designed with unbleached all-purpose flour in mind. I like to think that a good baker can make phenomenal bread (or cookies, cakes, etc.) with almost any flour. I use unbleached all-purpose flour at the bakery, and all of these recipes have been designed with that in mind. If you have a single-origin, hand-milled wheat of special provenance, by all means, use that. But you don't need to.

Water

If your water is potable, it will work fine. I have always used tap water to make breads and starters.

Salt for Bread

I prefer to use table salt (like Morton) or a flakier version (like kosher salt). These are finer in texture than coarse sea salt and dissolve most quickly into dough. In a pinch, any salt will do the job—NaCl is NaCl is NaCl. Salt affects dough in several different ways—it can slow down or encourage fermentation depending on the amount added (it is beneficial in extremely small quantities)—and it can even prevent dough mixed in a stand mixer from coming together quickly when added at the beginning of a mix. But every type of salt—coarse, fine, or flaky—will follow the same patterns.

Salt for Cooking

For cooking, I often use a mortar and pestle to grind down coarse sea salt into smaller granules. I love that the resulting granulation is uneven, so that there are small, fine bits as well as larger pieces. The occasional large piece will tend not to dissolve fully in food, which I love—that sudden, unexpected burst of saltiness.

Biga

Biga is my term for the type of sourdough starter I use. You will need to make this and have it on hand for baking the sourdough breads in this book. If you need to make a starter, it will take several days—and possibly a few tries—to get one going (see Refreshing the Starter, page 47). If you have a sourdough starter already, it will take a day or two to transform your liquid starter into a fermented dough, or *biga* (page 51). Some recipes call for "extremely fresh biga"—this indicates a young biga that has completely fermented (it will have just finished rising and have collapsed or started to collapse). It should be extremely bubbly and sweet smelling. At this point

it is particularly vigorous and active and able to do the quick and heavy lifting that some recipes require.

Wheat Bran

I almost always use wheat bran when dusting the towels or parchment on which doughs proof. It is much cleaner to use than flour (it is easy to sweep up, it doesn't turn into a paste when wet, and it comes cleanly off towels), and the pieces that stick to the dough and toast as the bread bake taste much better than clumps of flour. Please note that wheat bran (from the outside of a grain of wheat) is not the same thing as wheat germ (the innermost kernel). The bran is fibrous and dry; the germ has a high proportion of oil (if a grain of wheat were an egg, the germ would be the yolk) and does not store well. If you cannot find wheat bran in your grocery store, try a natural foods market, where wheat bran is often sold in bulk. Buy a large bag of it—at least a pound—as you'll go through it quickly if you're baking often. If you like to reuse things, it is perfectly acceptable to reuse the bran that your dough has rested on—as long as it is dry. Simply put it in a separate container and you can use it several times. (Bakers do this all the time and call the flour or bran used for such purposes "bench flour.")

Fast-Acting/Instant Yeast

Any of the foil packages or jars of active dry yeast that you find in the grocery store will work. I recommend fast-acting instant yeast, however, because of its very small granules, which dissolve and disperse quickly in the dough. (I do not recommend using cake yeast—sold, as you might imagine, refrigerated, in large cakes—because it tends to spoil quickly.)

EQUIPMENT

A Heavy Pot or Cloche with a Tight-Fitting Lid

For me, this is indispensable. Many of the breads featured in this book use my "oven within an oven" method—a heavy pot with a tight-fitting heavy lid that bakes in a blazing-hot oven. When the dough is enclosed in a hot, heavy pot, the steam that escapes from the dough is trapped inside the pot, allowing a good crust to form while keeping the interior crumb moist and airy. You'll need a 4½- to 5½-quart pot. There are many handsome designs on the market now, from the classic Lodge cast-iron Dutch ovens to the lovely cloche made by Emile Henry.

Kitchen Scale

If you are going to bake with sourdough, you will need a kitchen scale. It doesn't need to be fancy, but it ought to hold around 10 pounds (about 4.5 kilograms) and weigh in grams. A gram is much smaller than an ounce and so much more precise. (There are about 28 grams in 1 ounce.) All of my measurements for bread recipes are in grams. I provide equivalents in cups and tablespoons whenever possible, but I strongly urge you to consider weighing your ingredients on a scale rather than measuring them with cups. In addition to being much more accurate, weighing is also neater and easier (once one overcomes the aversion—if you have it—to using a scale). In addition, please note that when my sourdough culture, which I call a *biga*, is an ingredient in another recipe, the amount is given only in grams. This is because the volume of a biga changes tremendously over time, as it grows and collapses, and it is not possible to give accurate measurements for it in cups or tablespoons. A final plea: kitchen scales are inexpensive, easy to use, take up little space, and are the secret to great bread. Buy one today! OXO makes an 11-pound digital scale that I really like, usually available for around $50—but other, less expensive scales work just as well—as long as they weigh in grams!

Flexible Plastic Dough Scraper

A flexible plastic dough scraper is extremely helpful. Scrapers are easy to find online, incredibly cheap (about a dollar), and this is one of those things where the simpler the version, the better. Skip the fancy stainless-steel versions and buy the plastic ones, which curve and bend to help scoop dough out of a bowl. They also do a wonderful job of scraping dough off flat surfaces cleanly and quickly—saving your dough from rips and tears, and making cleanup easier. They are never essential but always useful.

Small Serrated Knife

A tomato knife with a scalloped-edged blade as opposed to one with jagged teeth works very well for scoring loaves.

1½-Quart Container

A bowl or other container this size will hug the dough and help it rise higher. A bowl that is much larger than the dough will allow the dough to expand sideways and flatten out as it ferments, rather than grow taller. A square clear plastic container like the kind Cambro makes is an invaluable way to gauge how much your dough has grown. These containers come in a variety of sizes—the 2- or 4-quart size works well for home baking—and are inexpensive and easily available online.

Cooling Racks

Cooling loaves and other baked goods on a wire rack keeps air circulating around the baked goods as they cool. This will prevent the dreaded soggy bottom.

Parchment Paper

Flat sheets come in a variety of sizes and are easier to work with than parchment paper on a roll. Look for these at restaurant supply stores and big wholesale clubs or for boxes of folded sheets at the grocer.

Tea Towels

Many of my bread recipes call for towels to enclose or cover the dough. Almost all kitchen towels work well—the only exception is terry cloth towels, whose loopy fibers tend to get stuck in the dough. Professional bakers traditionally rest their dough in linen, which I prefer, because dough is less likely to stick to it. Cotton is a fine alternative.

Stand Mixer with Paddle Attachment

Many people mix bread dough in a stand mixer. Usually they are mixing very stiff doughs and use the dough hook—a large metal hook. My doughs are different. They tend to be extremely well hydrated to produce an open, airy interior. The dough hook will not work for mixing these wet and sticky doughs. One day I was playing around with my KitchenAid stand mixer and discovered that the pastry paddle, which is sometimes referred to as a "flat beater," *does* work on my loose, messy doughs. The pastry paddle is a large triangle with rounded edges and a Y-shaped center. No bread in this book requires one of these, but if you have one, it does make for great, quick bread, and I have included instructions on how to use one in every case where it is possible. Please note that a handheld electric mixer is *not* an acceptable alternative for mixing bread doughs. It is simply not strong enough.

Additionally, the estimated times for mixing doughs in a stand mixer are those that correspond to my own model—a KitchenAid Professional 5 Plus. Other types of stand mixers (or newer or older versions of the same model) might do the job in more or less time than I have estimated. Please use the visual cues I have indicated as a guide if the estimated times seem off for your own stand mixer.

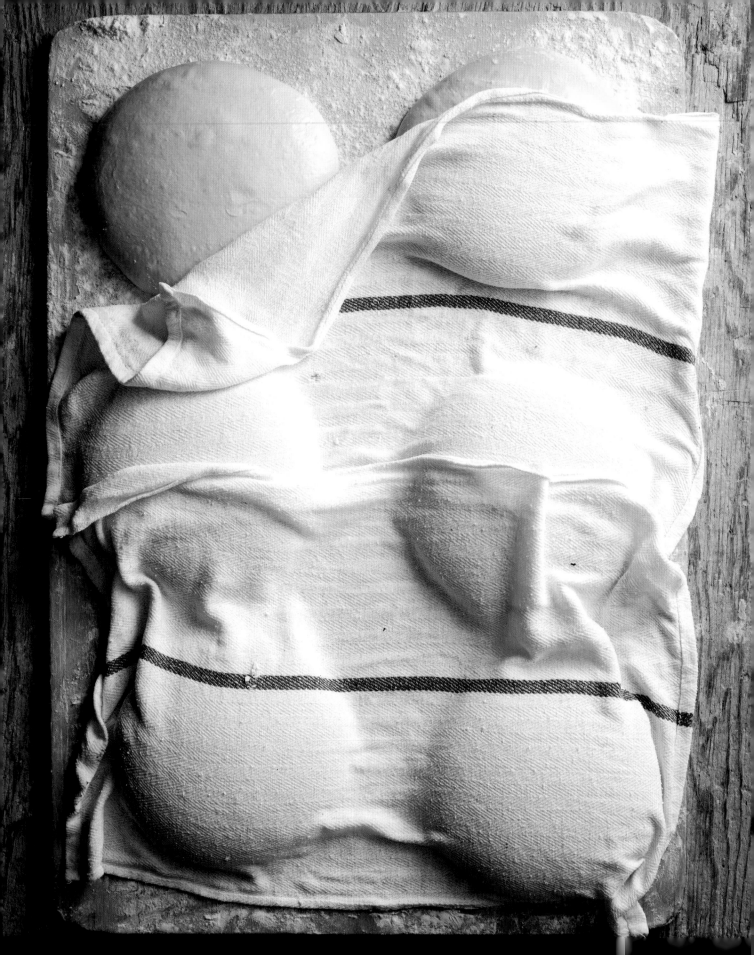

A BAKER'S REFERENCE

Biga

A hunk of naturally fermented dough I use to leaven bread. Italians use this word a bit differently, but I have been calling my "mother dough" *biga* for twenty-five years, and I am attached to the name.

Crumb

The inside of the bread.

Crust

The outside of the bread. I like mine dark, malty, and crackling.

Leavening

To *leaven* is to *raise*. There are many ways of raising a baked good, from packaged yeast to baking powder. Letting wild yeast and bacteria do the job is to make use of natural leavening.

Lid Removal

If you forget to set a timer, you can use this rough guideline for removing the lid from breads baked in a pot: When the smell of bread first wafts through your kitchen, it's time to take the lid off and continue baking until the crust is the color you like.

Mistakes

There is something to learn from every mistake. At least, this is how I look at it. I don't think there is any way to make great bread, every time, without making the occasional dud.

Even bakeries make mistakes. At Sullivan Street, we have a policy stipulating that no dough should be left behind (in other words, thrown away). If nothing else, a rogue dough can serve as great practice for scoring and shaping techniques. It is also far easier to dispose of a baked dough than an unbaked one, and an extra loaf can always be turned into breadcrumbs.

> **The One That Got Away:** One hot summer evening I arrived at the bakery to find that someone had broken our most important rule of dough disposal. An enormous batch of dough had been mixed, enough for hundreds of loaves, and something must have been wrong with the batch. But rather than cut it into loaves and bake it off as practice loaves for beginning bakers, as our policy instructs, someone had poured the entire batch into a

100-gallon compost bucket and left it outside on the street for the sanitation company to pick up. I do not know what the fatal flaw of this dough was, but it was clear that no one had forgotten the leavening. In the humid summer heat, the dough had acquired a life of its own. It had exploded up and out of the compost bucket and was bubbling quickly and enthusiastically down the street in the direction of Times Square. It was unclear whether its intentions were conquest or amusement. I marshaled all the extra hands I could, excavated the snow shovels from their summer storage spot, and we spent the rest of the evening wrangling the renegade dough back into the compost. Since then, we have all kept a keener eye on our mixing and our doughs.

Mixing

When mixing by hand, stir the ingredients together as quickly and violently as possible. I usually aim for 10 seconds or less. I like to think of it as introducing the flour and water to each other. You want to bring them into contact, but you do not want to *force* them together with prolonged mixing, which will damage the texture of the dough. The opposite is true when mixing in a stand mixer. Once the ingredients come together, turn the mixer on high and beat the dough until it becomes soft, clingy, and elastic.

Natural Fermentation

Also known as natural leavening or sourdough baking, natural fermentation is the process by which bacteria and yeast digest the sugars that comprise starches and turn them into carbon dioxide, alcohol, energy, and a beguiling array of flavoring compounds. The carbon dioxide produced by fermentation inflates bubbles in the dough and causes the dough to rise. The alcohols, esters, and acids produced by natural fermentation flavor the crumb and crust.

Patience

Especially in cooler weather, it may take many hours (or even days) for a dough to properly leaven. This can be frustrating if you are desperately awaiting bread, but on the bright side, remember that the long fermentation induced by the cold temperatures is a really good thing for the bread. The slower the dough ferments, the more beautifully the flavors will develop, and the more gorgeous, open—even transparent—your crumb will be. It is well worth waiting the extra hours for the bread to come up, even if it seems like it never will.

Scoring

To score a loaf of bread is to slash its top one or more times, right before it goes in the oven. Scoring the dough creates a soft, elastic line (or lines) to guide its expansion. It also allows steam a place to exit the dough. Many loaves benefit from a simple score, but there are some, such as the delicate Ciabatta (page 85), that should not be scored. A single slash would deflate it. For some breads, scoring is optional. Tuscan Bread (page 71) and Pane Bianco (page 89), for instance, look nice when scored—but if they are unscored, they will simply burst open in the oven in an unpredictable way, which is also beautiful.

Like everything else, scoring takes a bit of practice. Here are some pointers: Use a serrated tomato or paring knife, 4 to 6 inches long. (Many people use a razor, but I find these rather dangerous.) Put the whole blade of the knife against the dough, not just the tip. Slash deeply and decisively; I usually aim for a slash at least ½ inch deep.

Shaping

Giving shape to a loose mass of dough is the act of shaping it. Shaping requires a delicate balance: The less the dough is handled, the better. The more it is handled and tugged at, the more likely the delicate structure within will deflate. (*See also* Tension.)

Any of the loaves that are described in this book as rounds could also be shaped into a tube or an oval. For instructions, follow the directions for shaping a Pullman loaf (page 58) or brioche loaf (page 107), and let the loaf proof on a towel or piece of parchment, then transfer to a preheated oval pot with a heavy lid, and bake according to the recommended time and temperature.

Speed Control

Naturally leavened bread can sometimes be hard to plan for. If a dough is taking longer to come up than I expected, either I try to speed it up by putting it someplace pleasantly warm (a sunny spot outside, in the oven with the utility light on or a steaming bowl of water near it) or I try to slow it down even further so that I can come back to it when I am ready. I often make use of the coldest room in the house, or a windowsill with the window cracked open, to hold a dough overnight until I am ready to shape or bake it, and this method often delivers some of my best homemade bread. In extremely hot places (like Florida in the summer) I will even resort to storing a shaped loaf in the refrigerator overnight.

Stand Mixers

All doughs in this book that are mixed in a stand mixer use the paddle attachment (also called the flat beater or pastry paddle). Please do not use the dough hook attachment or attempt to use a handheld electric mixer. Such endeavors will end in mess, frustration, and possibly a broken mixer. Additionally, the estimated times for mixing doughs in a stand mixer are those that correspond to my own model—a KitchenAid Professional 5 Plus. Other types of stand mixers (or newer or older versions of the same model) might do the job in more or less time than I have estimated. Please use the visual cues I have indicated as a guide if the estimated times seem off for your own stand mixer.

Starter

Mixing a slurry of flour and water creates the perfect growth medium for wild yeasts and other helpful microbes. I usually have success mixing equal parts flour and water and allowing them to ferment (page 43). Some people may prefer the more reliable method of acquiring the yeast naturally present on a fresh fruit or vegetable (page 44). It is possible to acquire starter from acquaintances and friendly businesses, but bear in mind that beyond sparing yourself the hassle of starting one yourself, this may convey no long-term advantages. A starter will usually adapt to its environment, and become populated by the sort of yeasts and bacteria that are found in your kitchen and that thrive in its climate. Many bakers keep a liquid starter on hand and mix it into their dough, but I prefer to thicken my starter (add flour) to slow down its growth rate. My starter is more of a dough than a liquid, and is called, in the Italian fashion, a *biga*.

Summer

Fermentation speeds up in warmer weather. This makes the bread-baking process go faster, but a fast fermentation can also mean that you need to keep a careful eye on your dough. If it rises too much in the leavening or proofing stages, it may become so big that it is unable to support itself and collapses. A liquid starter, biga, or bread dough may all become quite sour if heat-loving bacteria come to outnumber the wild yeasts.

Tension

Tucking the corners of a loaf under it to shape it into a round, or rolling up a loaf to shape it into an oval not only gives the dough a defined shape but also creates surface tension on the exterior of the dough. This is essential for getting a good rise, or "oven spring" in the oven. The surface tension prevents the dough from spreading sideways as it rests and allows the dough to save all of its remaining energy for the oven, when the first blast of heat and subsequent explosion of gas bubbles will force the loaf to expand the only way it can: upward.

Water

Every brand and batch of flour can be a bit different. Sometimes, a particular flour will absorb a bit more water than the flour with which I have tested these recipes and it may be necessary to add a tablespoon or so extra water to the dough as you mix. You should expect to have flour on the sides of the bowl when you mix a dough by hand, and you should also expect to end your quick, vigorous mix with a shaggy, messy dough that does not form a round. But if you mix the flour and water together—either by hand or in a stand mixer—and find they are not combining well, this is a sign to add a touch more water (a spoonful or so). At other times, you may find the dough too wet to come together, in which case you should add a tablespoon or so of flour.

Winter

Doughs made solely with biga slow down dramatically when outdoor temperatures drop. For this reason, I give suggestions for how much to increase the biga in these breads (such as the Truccio, page 93, or Pane Bianco, page 89) when outdoor temperatures are quite cold (below 39°F). I use outdoor temperatures as a guide, because indoor temperatures in the winter often fluctuate dramatically within a house. Areas near vents may be quite hot, while drafty spots in other areas may be many degrees cooler. (*See also* Patience.)

The one naturally leavened bread that is an exception to this rule is the Pane Toscano (page 71). The percentage of biga is so high in this loaf that it leavens relatively quickly even in cold temperatures.

On the left is a starter just mixed. The flour and water have been stirred into a soupy paste. In the center is a starter a few days old. It has separated into flour and water, and begun to ferment, pushing some of the flour to the top of the water in a foamy-looking raft. On the right is an even older starter. It rose, collapsed, and separated again into flour and water.

3

MAKING A STARTER

AS I'VE MENTIONED, WHEN I BAKE WITH SOURDOUGH, I USE A PIECE OF DOUGH (biga), rather than a liquid starter as the leavening. But the old piece of sourdough has to start somewhere, and the easiest way to catch a bit of wild yeast and its bacterial companions is in a liquid medium. If you are already blessed with a healthy starter, refresh it (page 47), then make biga (page 51), and you will be ready to bake. If you do not have a starter, here are two ways to make one. The first method is simply flour and water. It is my favorite way to make a starter because it is the simplest. The second method is often faster and more reliable, but it involves rubbing some yeast off of a fruit or vegetable. I encourage you to try one or both of these methods, and to think of them as good, clean countertop adventures. Every time you make a starter, the conditions and results will be a little bit different. My own kitchen and refrigerator are often cluttered with jars of flour and water in various stages of fermentation, not because I need them, but just because I am fascinated by this simple but nevertheless astonishing process.

A SIMPLE LIQUID STARTER

I like to start a sourdough in a glass jar. It's remarkable to watch the flour and water slowly separate and then, even more slowly, bubble, foam, and separate again.

YIELD: 1 liquid sourdough starter   EQUIPMENT: An extremely clean 16-ounce mason jar

100 grams (½ cup) room-temperature (65° to 70°F) water

50 grams flour (heaping ⅓ cup)

1. Mix together the flour and water and leave at room temperature. Cover loosely if desired.

2. Wait. The flour and water will separate. After 1 to 5 days (the colder the weather, the longer this takes) the flour and water will begin to ferment and you will see a few minuscule bubbles—fermentation has begun! The bubbles will begin to push the flour toward the surface, so that it mixes with the water. The fermentation will gradually speed up and soon you will have a bubbly, frothy, yeasty-smelling soup.

3. The foam will rise and expand, and then it will collapse. If given enough time, it will again separate into flour and water. (If you go a day or so without looking at your starter, you may miss the entire spectacle, so play crime-scene detective and look for the telltale sign that fermentation has happened: a foamy ring around the inside of the jar, above the starter).

4. Once the starter has risen and fallen, it's ready to refresh (see page 47).

A FASTER LIQUID STARTER

My First Starter and Second Mother: My first attempt to make a starter on my own was in the autumn of 1992. I had been staying near Milan, but a bakery I loved in Tuscany offered me a chance to train with them, and so I made my way back to the small town of San Gimignano, near Florence. It was torrentially wet, and I arrived in the midst of nonstop rain. I was staying with some friends who happened to be (peaceful) Italian anarchists, and the monotony of the weather coupled with the subversive social culture left me thinking I really ought to cultivate my own sourdough culture.

I noticed that there was Tuscan kale growing outside (Tuscan kale has long, flat leaves and is also known as *dinosaur kale*, *black kale*, or *lacinato kale*). The kale leaves had a copious yeast bloom on them—the kind of opaque, powdery film that you may also find on the outside of plums, grapes, blueberries, and other fruits. I was curious about the yeast and wondered if it might be a helpful addition to my sourdough experiment. I filled a bowl with water and a few of the kale leaves. I stirred in some flour, covered it with a plate, and left it in the root cellar. When I uncovered it four days later, it had become a frothy dough that smelled of sulfur and alcohol. I had a starter! This starter became my biga, or "mother dough," and has leavened all Sullivan Street Bakery bread since 1994.

This is another way to make a starter. It is often possible—but not as reliable—to make a sourdough starter using flour and water alone, but I suggest finding a fruit or vegetable with a nice yeasty bloom on the surface to speed up the process. Yeast on kale or a piece of fruit looks and acts much like sunblock—it's a thin white layer that repels water. It's easy to rub off and most likely to be found on a fruit or vegetable that is organic and has not been handled too much.

Whether using a fruit and vegetable bloom or simply flour and water, this method works best when indoor temperatures are 55° to 70°F. If it's much hotter than that in your kitchen, it can be hard for the right sort of bacteria to form a stable population. You can tell within a few days—a healthy starter will smell sweet and yeasty, while a sourdough with a problematic community of bacteria will smell rather like extremely malodorous feet. So if your kitchen is hot, I recommend doing a 6-hour rotation and keeping the starter on the countertop for 6 hours, then in the refrigerator for 6 hours, or overnight, if necessary, and so forth. If you already have a starter, refresh it (see page 47), ensure that it smells sweet and yeasty (if not, keep refreshing until it does), and then make biga (page 51).

(CONTINUES)

A Bloom-Based Starter, in Pictures

1 Choose a fruit or vegetable with a yeasty bloom on it.

2 The yeast "bloom" gives this purple cabbage leaf a dusty white sheen and acts as a water repellant.

3 Immerse your fruits or leaves in water, and rub off the bloom.

4 You will see a different color where you have rubbed away the bloom.

5 Pour away half the water, and add the flour to what remains.

6 Mix together.

7 Transfer to a mason jar, cup, or small bowl, and store in a cool place.

8 Fermentation will leave the top pock-marked with bubbles.

YIELD: 1 liquid sourdough starter   EQUIPMENT: An extremely clean 16-ounce mason jar

2 kale, cabbage, or collard green leaves, abundantly covered with a bloom of yeast—an opaque, bluish mist that coats the smooth surface of a leaf or fruit and can easily be wiped away

200 grams (⅞ cup) room-temperature (65° to 70°F) water

50 grams (heaping ⅓ cup) unbleached all-purpose flour

1. Thoroughly wash and dry your hands.

2. Immerse the kale leaves in the water in a small bowl. Using your fingers, firmly rub off as much of the yeast bloom as possible. Usually it's more abundant on the underside of the leaf, but it can be on top as well. Shake off any excess water. You'll notice that the bloom acts as a repellent to the water, and once the bloom has been removed, the leaf itself will get wet.

3. Discard the leaves and half of the water and add the flour. Stir. Pour into a 16-ounce mason jar, placing the lid on loosely. Store in a cool (55° to 70°F) place for 2 to 6 days, until the mixture begins to bubble and rise. It may bubble, rise, and collapse in your absence, so look for the sign that it has happened: a residue on the sides of the jar above the water level.

4. Once the starter has risen and collapsed, begin the first refreshment (see page 47). It may require a series of refreshments to cultivate the starter to the point that it smells yeasty and works reliably. With each successive refreshment you will note that the starter gets stronger and has more vitality.

REFRESHING THE STARTER

Why refresh a starter? Because you don't want the starter itself; you want the wonderful microbes that live in it—that particular colony of wild yeast and bacteria that you have adopted. To refresh means to take a small amount of the original starter and give it fresh flour and water, providing the perfect environment in which the yeasts and bacteria may flourish. The larger their numbers, the stronger the starter, and the stronger the starter, the higher and faster your bread will rise. The refreshed starter will be livelier than the first, and it will ferment much faster.

It is important when transferring the starter to a new jar after it has been refreshed that the sides of the jar remain clean. Any starter on the wall of the jar may encourage the growth of surface molds.

10 grams (about 1 tablespoon) fully fermented starter (page 43 or 44)

100 grams (½ cup) room-temperature (65° to 70°F) water

50 grams (heaping ⅓ cup) unbleached all-purpose flour

1. Once your original starter has risen and collapsed, the flour will settle at the bottom of the jar with a pale layer of water on top and a pad of bloom on the surface. Give it a good stir to mix it up and transfer 1 tablespoon of it to a small bowl. (Save the remaining starter in the refrigerator as insurance in case of spills or accidents. Tightly covered, a starter will keep for weeks or even months refrigerated.) Add the fresh water and flour and mix thoroughly. Pour into a clean 16-ounce jar. Cover loosely and let the mixture sit at room temperature.

2. In time, the flour and water will bubble and rise. It might take hours, or in some cases days. Eventually it becomes a very bubbly, spongy, well-aerated batter. The starter should smell strongly of yeast and faintly of champagne. It should taste a bit tart—but not too much. It may smell sour and pungent—like overripe cheese—but if it smells extremely unpleasant or develops mold, start over with some of the reserved starter put away in the refrigerator. If you doubt the health, vitality, or strength of your starter, repeat this step—refreshing the starter— a few times, anywhere from two to seven, until it smells yeasty and has a gentle smack of tartness. This may take several refreshments. The starter is now ready to use for making my own, doughier version of a starter—which I refer to using the Italian term *biga* (page 51).

From left to right:

A newly mixed starter that has begun to separate into flour and water.

A day later, with no stirring, the flour and water have completely separated. As the first few bubbles appear, it should start to smell yeasty.

Several days later, fermentation has taken off, and the starter may smell increasingly sour. Bubbles of carbon dioxide have pushed the flour to the surface of the water, giving it a spongy appearance.

Fermentation ends, the bubbles of carbon dioxide burst, the flour sinks, and the flour and water begin to separate again. This starter is ready to stir together and refresh.

Biga, pockmarked with bubbles, fully fermented, and ready to use.

"JIM'S BIGA"

a stiff starter

In Italy, the word *biga* is used to describe an assortment of "pre-ferments"—the already-fermented pieces of dough that are added to bread doughs to speed up fermentation and add flavor to the finished bread. At Sullivan Street Bakery we use the name *biga* to refer to our own doughy starter. It is made of flour, water, salt, and yesterday's biga.

There is no precise schedule for making biga—both at home and in the bakery, I make a new batch only when running out of the old one. To get a biga started at home, you will need a dab of healthy sourdough starter.

I infinitely prefer using biga to a liquid starter for three reasons: (1) it's what I learned as I traveled around Italy as an impressionable young man; (2) it's more stable than the liquid starter many people use, not to mention cleaner to work with; and (3) it's easier to keep around than a starter: you don't need to feed it, remember it, or stir it. At the bakery we wait at least 24 hours from the time it is mixed before using a new batch of biga, but you can often wait longer—a healthy biga that is tightly covered and stored in the refrigerator will stay ready to use for a week.

70 grams (scant ⅓ cup) room-temperature (65° to 70°F) water

10 grams (scant 1 tablespoon) refreshed fermented starter

100 grams (½ cup plus 3 tablespoons) unbleached all-purpose flour

0.1 gram (a tiny pinch) fine sea salt

1. Mix together the water and the refreshed starter in a small bowl. Add the flour and a few grains of salt. (Use just a tiny pinch, please—a bit of salt will speed up fermentation, but a heavy dose of salt will slow it down.) The dough will look lumpy, uneven, and small. Cover the bowl and prepare to wait about 24 hours for it to triple in size. Don't be dismayed if nothing happens for the first 12 hours—it takes a while to get going, but once the fermentation starts, it will take off, and it is likely to grow more in the final 4 hours than it did in the first 16.

2. Poke at it and taste it—a fully fermented biga is pleasantly tangy with a fantastically airy, spongy, viscous structure. It will feel tacky, and it will taste and smell deliciously yeasty with a gentle smack of tartness—a bit like beer, but without any bitterness. At this point it's ready to use. You may note color changes in the biga as the top layer dries out and oxidizes a bit; this is perfectly fine and to be expected.

(CONTINUES)

Storing Biga in the Short Term

If your biga is ready to use and you are not ready to use it, that's fine. This is the wonderful thing about a biga—once it's ready there is a long window of time where it stays ready. It keeps unrefrigerated for several days.

My one caveat is that if your kitchen temperature is above 72°F, it is probably a good idea to keep your biga in the refrigerator or someplace else that's cool. Extended time in a warm temperature will eventually promote the proliferation of the heat-loving bacteria that are part of the starter. They aren't harmful, but they will multiply faster than the wild yeast, so that your bread will take longer to leaven and the deeply sour, acidic flavors of bacterial fermentation will overpower the milder flavors of a well-balanced rise.

Keep the biga cool enough that it tastes and smells tart, yeasty, and sweet. A very healthy biga that has been used and refreshed consistently will often keep for several weeks—or even longer in the refrigerator. You can judge the state of the biga by smelling and tasting it. When it tastes painfully acidic, for instance, it is time to make a new batch.

Storing Biga in the Long Term

If you'd like to store a biga for a matter of weeks or months, cover it tightly and store in the back of the refrigerator. A biga may discolor slightly or become a bit like glue in texture. These things are fine—as are smells that range from yeasty to alcoholic. Twenty-four hours before you plan to bake, take a teaspoon of biga and follow the steps for making more biga (page 53). Once this biga has tripled in size it is ready to use.

MAKING MORE BIGA

You can make biga from anything that has natural leavening in it: starter, fresh or old biga, or naturally fermented bread dough. When your biga runs low or you notice that your existing biga is beginning to acidify, turn gray, or separate into flour and water, it will soon be time to make more. If you accidentally use all your biga, and have nothing left to make more with, just save a pinch of dough (prior to baking it) from the bread that you're making and use that in place of the 5 grams of biga called for below. Any bread dough—even brioche dough with egg or a mixed dough with both instant yeast and biga in it—will work fine. The desirable microbes will prevail.

5 grams (about 1 teaspoon) fermented biga or old dough

70 grams (scant ⅓ cup) room-temperature (65° to 70°F) water

100 grams (½ cup plus 3 tablespoons) unbleached all-purpose flour

0.1 gram (a tiny pinch) fine sea salt*

***If you are using a bit of dough rather than biga, omit the salt; the pinch of dough contains sufficient salt.**

Dissolve the biga or dough in the water and mix with the flour and salt. Wait until the mixture has risen (about 24 hours on average), and then the new biga is ready to use for baking.

A Note on the First Loaf

Whether this is the first loaf you ever make from this book or the first loaf you make after a while, after having resurrected a biga that has been stored in the refrigerator for some time, I recommend pinching off a piece of *the first batch of fully leavened dough*, immediately before shaping it, to make a new batch of biga. (Keep the old biga handy as backup until the new batch is ready.) Repeat the process for your next round of baking. When a bit of biga leavens a loaf, it grows in strength and numbers (of beneficial microbes). The more often a biga is used, and the more frequently it is regenerated, the stronger and more stable it becomes.

Waiting

If you are chomping at the bit to get baking while your starter and biga are not yet ready, jump right in with the recipes for Milk Bread (page 58), Golden Flax Bread (page 63), pizzas (Chapter 5), Bran and Blackberry Muffins (page 140), the Orange Olive-Oil Cake (page 142), or the tarts, cake, and cookies found in Chapter 9.

Naturally leavened brioche (page 107).

4

SULLIVAN STREET
BREADS

THE BREADS IN THIS CHAPTER ARE A DIVERSE LOT: SOME, SUCH AS THE
Pugliese (page 76) and Ciabatta (page 85), are my own versions of Italian classics.
Others—such as the Multigrani (page 99) and "wastED" bread (page 112)—are
inventions that became our own traditions—and, indeed, some of my favorite breads.

Many of the breads in this chapter are leavened with sourdough and the tiniest
bit of instant (or other fast-acting) baker's yeast. In some cases, such as with ciabatta,
this is because I love the medley of flavors created by the dual sources of fermentation. In other cases, such as with Hamilton Buns (page 101), it is because I like the
faster, more predictable rise delivered by even a pinch of baker's yeast. If you are a
sourdough purist and want to omit the instant yeast, that works fine in every case—
simply leave it out and add a few extra hours to the expected fermentation time. A
couple of these breads—the Faster Truccio (page 97) and basic brioche dough (page
107)—require "extremely fresh" biga, which refers to young biga that has only just
risen and collapsed and is at the height of its powers.

The first two recipes here, for Pane al Latte (page 58) and Pane di Lino (page
63), are no-knead loaves made with baker's yeast. They are not sourdough breads,
but I include them here because I often bake them when I am away from home and
waiting for my biga to rise and impatient to have bread. If you are impatient, too—or
would just like an easy, no-knead bread to practice on, start with these. They are
simple, quick, and don't even have the bother of the hot pot in the oven, since they
proof and bake in their tidy little Pullman compartments.

No-knead milk bread (page 58).

PANE AL LATTE

milk bread

Pane al latte is based on a bread from the Lazio region of Italy that is now made throughout the country. It is enriched with milk and honey and is often used in roll form for making small sandwiches because it's soft and sweet. When baked in a Pullman loaf pan, this bread comes out perfectly rectangular, so it is just the right size for toast or very precise sandwiches.

YIELD: One 9-inch-long Pullman loaf; 1¼ pounds
EQUIPMENT: A 9-by-4-inch Pullman loaf pan with lid, if making a loaf

- 300 grams (1¼ cups) whole milk, plus milk for brushing rolls (see variation)
- 10 grams (1½ teaspoons) honey
- 75 grams (⅓ cup) room-temperature (65° to 70°F) water
- 395 grams (2¾ cups) unbleached all-purpose flour, plus flour for dusting
- 5 grams (1 tablespoon) wheat bran

- 6 grams (1 teaspoon) fine sea salt
- 3 grams (1 teaspoon) fast-acting/instant yeast*
- Olive oil for the pan

* When outdoor temperatures drop below 39°F, use 1½ teaspoons of yeast and an extra tablespoon of water

1. Scald the milk in a small saucepan over medium heat: bring the milk just to a boil, then immediately remove it from the heat. Put the honey and water in a medium bowl, pour in the scalded milk, and stir. Let cool until tepid, about 90°F.

2. Whisk the flour, bran, salt, and yeast together in a large bowl to combine.

3. When the milk mixture has cooled, pour the liquid into the dry ingredients and vigorously and quickly stir together with a spoon or spatula. Stop the moment it comes together into a wet and shaggy dough. If any dough is left on the side of the bowl or stuck to the spoon, scrape the dough off and drop it into the rest of the dough. Cover the bowl with a tea towel and let rest for 20 minutes at room temperature. Dust the edges of the dough with a little flour and fold the edges into the center. Flip the dough over, re-cover, and let sit until it has doubled in size—2 to 4 hours. When ready it will feel soft, fluffy, and spongelike. Before shaping, dust the edges with flour again, scrape the sides of the dough off the bowl, and fold into the center. Let rest for 30 to 60 minutes or until it begins to grow again.

(CONTINUES)

No-Knead Milk Bread, in Pictures

1 Measure the water and honey into a bowl.

2 Add the scalded milk and allow to cool.

3 Weigh the dry ingredients into a separate bowl and whisk together.

4 Pour the cooled liquids into the bowl of dry ingredients.

5 Quickly mix together.

6 Cover for 20 minutes.

7 Dust the edges of the dough with flour.

8 Gently fold the edges of the dough in toward the center.

(CONTINUES)

9 Oil a Pullman pan and its lid.

10 When ready to shape the dough, turn it out onto a well-floured work surface.

11 Flour the top of the dough.

12 Flatten the dough into a rough circle, and then fold the edges in to make a rectangle.

13 Now take the two corners farthest from you and fold them in to make a triangle tip.

14 Roll the tip toward you, using your thumbs to gently stretch the cylinder away from you and create a little tension in the dough.

15 Place the dough seam-side down in the oiled pan and press down lightly to fill the corners.

16 Wait for the dough to reach the top of the pan, then refrigerate or bake.

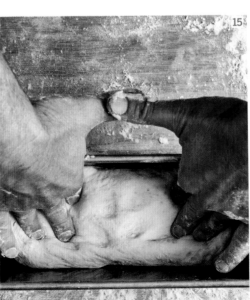

4. Oil the Pullman pan and lid. Carefully turn the dough out onto a lightly floured work surface. Lightly flour your hands and the edges of the dough. Take care not to tear the dough even slightly and, using a dough scraper, gently pry it from the sides of the bowl. Lightly flour the top of the dough and pat it down to flatten it into an approximately 8-inch round. Take the left side and fold it across the dough, two-thirds of the way to the right side. Fold the right side of the dough two-thirds of the way across the dough to the left side. Gently pat down the dough again and make a tube by folding down the two corners farthest from you to make a small triangle. Pat down the tip of the triangle very firmly and then roll it toward you. Continue rolling the entire dough toward you until you have a 9-inch-long cylinder. Put the dough seam side down into the lightly oiled Pullman pan and press the dough down gently to fill the corners. Slide the lid on to cover the pan, leaving a small slit open so you can keep an eye on the dough. Let the dough proof at room temperature for 1 to 1½ hours. The dough is ready when it reaches the top of the rim of the pan. (At this point it can also be refrigerated overnight and baked off first thing in the morning. Allow the loaf to come to room temperature for about 30 minutes.) Slide the lid completely shut.

5. Heat the oven to 400°F. Bake the bread, covered, for 45 to 50 minutes. When it's done, it will be golden brown and pulling away from the sides of the pan. Remove from the oven and remove the lid. Wait 5 minutes and remove from the pan. Allow the loaf to cool on a wire rack before slicing.

VARIATION

FOR LITTLE ROLLS OR HAMBURGER BUNS

For little rolls, when the dough is ready to shape after step 3, divide it into 12 even pieces (or 6, for hamburger buns), using a dough scraper (alternatively, dust two fingers with flour and pretend they are scissors—it works well and is surprisingly fun). Fold the dough under and into itself to make taut little balls; but do not handle the dough so much that the dough gets sticky—this means you're stretching too much. Put the shaped balls of dough onto a sheet pan that has been lined with parchment paper or lightly oiled. Allow the rolls to double in volume—about an hour and a half. Heat the oven to 450°F, brush the tops of the rolls with a little milk, and bake the rolls for about 15 minutes (20 minutes for hamburger buns) or until the tops have colored.

No-knead flax bread.

PANE DI LINO
golden flax bread

I love the flavor of flax. These days flax has a reputation as a superfood, and somehow, in the enthusiasm over its health benefits, its lovely sweet, mild, nutty flavor has been forgotten. I particularly prefer the flavor and appearance of golden, rather than brown, flaxseeds. Flax has been used alongside wheat in bread baking for much of human history—I think that makes it an ancient grain—and I'm sure one of the reasons it's been used with wheat is that is has such a pleasant taste. This is another perfect sandwich bread.

YIELD: One 9-inch-long Pullman loaf; 1¼ pounds   EQUIPMENT: A 9-by-4-inch Pullman loaf pan with lid

370 grams (2½ cups) unbleached all-purpose flour, plus flour for dusting

25 grams (¼ cup) milled flaxseeds

5 grams (1 tablespoon) wheat bran

3 grams (1 teaspoon) fast-acting/instant yeast

6 grams (1 teaspoon) fine sea salt

300 grams (1⅓ cups) water

5 grams (1 teaspoon) grapeseed, olive, or walnut oil, plus oil for the pan and lid

1. Whisk the flour, flax meal, wheat bran, yeast, and salt together in a medium bowl to combine. Whisk the water and oil together in a larger bowl. Pour the dry ingredients into the water and oil and mix quickly with a spoon. Within seconds the dough should come together. It will look lumpy and shaggy. Cover loosely and let rest for 20 minutes at room temperature. Dust the edges of the dough with flour and fold them into the center. Flip the dough over, re-cover, and allow to double in size at room temperature—about 4 hours. It should be springy, sticky, and elastic. If you tug at it, it should pull back. Flour the edges of the dough, scrape them off the side of the bowl, and fold them into the center of the dough. Flip the dough over and let rest, covered with a tea towel at room temperature, for an hour or until it looks like it is beginning to grow again.

2. Use a teaspoonful of oil to coat the Pullman pan and lid. Lightly flour a work surface and turn the dough out onto it. Lightly flour the top of the dough and pat it down to flatten it into an approximately 8-inch round. Take the left side and fold it across the dough, two-thirds of the way to the right side. Fold the right side of the dough two-thirds of the way across the dough to the left side, gently pat down the dough again, and make a tube by folding down the two corners farthest from you to make a small triangle. Pat down the tip of the triangle

(CONTINUES)

very firmly and then roll it toward you. Continue rolling the entire dough toward you until you have a 9-inch-long cylinder. Put the dough seam side down into the Pullman pan and press the dough down gently to fill the corners. Slide the lid on to cover the pan, leaving a small slit open so you can keep an eye on the dough. Let the dough proof at room temperature for 1½ to 3 hours. The dough is ready when it reaches the top of the rim of the pan. (At this point it can also be refrigerated overnight and baked off first thing in the morning. Allow refrigerated loaves to sit at room temperature for 30 minutes before baking.) Slide the lid completely shut.

3. Heat oven to 450°F. Put the Pullman pan in the oven gently, taking care not to disturb the dough. Bake for 45 minutes with the lid on throughout. When the bread is ready, it will be a light, golden, tan, sandy color—think Desert Storm buff. The finished loaf will look like it's just ready to pull away from the side of the pan. Once you take the bread out of the oven and remove the lid, remove the bread from the pan within 5 minutes. (If the loaf sits in the pan longer, condensation in the pan will make the sides of the bread wet and soggy.) Cool on a wire rack before slicing.

> **Flax meal:** Bob's Red Mill and several other suppliers sell bags of golden flax meal, but you might also buy golden flax seeds and grind your own, if desired.

PIZZA BIANCA ALLA ROMANA, VERSION 1

handmade pizza with salt and olive oil, as made in Rome
(This recipe requires the stiff starter, or biga, on page 51.)

It's very hard not to like this bread. Not only is it soft, chewy, and addictive, but it is also one of the easiest breads to make with the least amount of equipment. The way this is made in Rome, it is 6 feet long and spectacular. When you order a piece, it's cut in front of you. We make it that way in the bakery too, but since I don't know anyone with a 6-foot oven at home, I've adapted the recipe to give you two 12-inch rounds of fluffy, dimpled pizza dough coated in sea salt and olive oil. The version here is naturally leavened and made entirely by hand. If you would prefer to make this with instant yeast in a stand mixer, please see the recipe on page 118.

Is one version better than the other? Not at all. Use the technique that allows you to make the best bread with the time and equipment you've got. I have made pizza bianca more ways than I can remember—both of my previous books include different versions of this bread—and varied the means, the technique, and the recipe according to the equipment I had available and the amount of time I had to work with.

Stretching Out, or "Opening," the Dough

The pizza dough we often see in pizzerias around the United States are very stiff doughs that come out of the refrigerator, full of additives and preservatives. They need to be tossed and rolled out with rolling pins and can be beaten down a little bit. My dough is quite different. It is not refrigerated (although it's fine to do that if you need to slow done the fermentation), nor is it stiff. It is very wet and loose. (I would not recommend throwing it into the air!)

When you go to stretch the dough into a circle, think of pulling it out, rather than flattening it. It will be delicate and wobbly, and if you flatten it, it may never recover. It will already be in a rough circle by this point, and all you'll need to do is gently tug at the edges to pull it into a larger circle. This dough has a tendency to pull back and resist. Try to stretch the dough just a little bigger than you think you'll need it.

I never aim for a perfect circle. If you don't have a peel to slide the pizza into the oven, an inverted sheet pan works in a pinch.

YIELD: Two 12-inch round pizzas   EQUIPMENT: A pizza stone and a 12-inch-wide peel

(CONTINUES)

Pizza bianca by hand.

400 grams (2¾ cups) unbleached all-purpose flour, plus flour for shaping

350 grams (1¼ cups) room-temperature (65° to 70°F) water

5 grams (1 teaspoon) sugar

5 grams (scant 1 teaspoon) fine sea salt

100 grams biga (page 51)

Extra virgin olive oil for brushing the bowl and pizzas

8 grams (1⅛ teaspoons) coarse sea salt

Fresh rosemary for serving (optional)

1. Whisk together the flour, sugar, and sea salt in a large bowl. In a separate bowl, whisk together the water and biga until the biga is fully dissolved and the water is very bubbly. Pour in the contents of the flour bowl and mix quickly and vigorously with a wooden spoon or rubber spatula. The dough will be bumpy and stringy looking. Cover the bowl with a tea towel and let the dough rest for 20 minutes at room temperature. Dust the edges of the dough with flour and fold them in toward the center of the bowl. Turn the dough over, cover, and let sit at room temperature for 5 to 7 hours, until it has increased in size by a third and is visibly bubbling.

2. Dust flour over two 12-by-16-inch pieces of parchment paper. Sift a little flour over the risen dough in the bowl. Lightly flour your hands. Using a dough scraper, divide the dough in half. Pinch off one half of the dough and, with gravity's help, form the dough into a taut ball and place seam side down on one piece of the floured parchment. Dust a bit more flour onto the paper if needed, so that there is a coating of flour on the paper all around the dough. Repeat with the second half of the dough and second piece of parchment.

3. Use a pastry brush to lightly coat the centers of the tops of each round of dough with olive oil. (Leave a margin of 2 inches around the perimeter; the oil will spread on its own.) Sprinkle the coarse sea salt on top of the oil. Let the dough rounds sit, uncovered, at room temperature until they have doubled in size, 1 to 3 hours. When they are ready, the dough rounds will be large, bubbly, expansive, and clearly full of gas. Place a pizza stone on the middle rack of the oven and heat it to 500°F.

4. Dust the tops of the doughs lightly with flour and gently pull the dough outward with both hands so that it stretches to about 8 inches in diameter. I call this movement "opening the dough." Now for 10 seconds of fun: Stick out all ten of your fingers like you're going to try to walk across the table with them and "dock," or dimple, both doughs by plunging your fingers into them very firmly, three or four times for each dough.

(CONTINUES)

Note on docking: The perfect amount of docking, or dimpling the dough, will give pizza bianca a sublime texture—pliant, soft, and bubbly. Too much docking will create a hard disk. Here is how I recommend doing it: press all 10 of your fingers firmly into one of the doughs. Press quite hard—enough to feel the surface below and leave a firm impression in the dough—but not so hard that you rip a hole in the dough. Repeat three or four times and then do the same for the other dough. The impressions will turn into craters and valleys and give the finished surface the appearance of a lunar landscape.

5. Place one docked pizza dough on parchment on the peel. Oil or flour your fingertips and dock the dough again, with both hands, about three times. Very gently, use your fingertips to pull the dough outward all around—it should stretch evenly to make a rough circle that nearly reaches the edges of the parchment and is about 12 inches in diameter.

6. Open the oven, line up the far end of the peel with the far end of the pizza stone, and shimmy and shake the dough and the parchment onto the stone. Bake for 10 to 12 minutes or until the top of the dough is browning and the valleys made by your fingertips are pale and golden. Slide the peel under the pizza and transfer it to a wire rack to cool for 5 minutes. If you don't have a wire rack, lean the pizza on its side for a few minutes. This will allow the bottom to cool and prevent it from becoming soft.

Now that the peel is free, place the second pizza on parchment and repeat the docking and stretching. Once you get comfortable handling the wet dough you can stop using the parchment. Bake the second pizza. Brush the warm pizzas generously with olive oil and a sprinkle of rosemary needles, if desired, and serve.

Note: I also like to use large slices of pizza bianca—split open lengthwise like a pita— for sandwiches such as the breakfast sandwiches in Chapter 6 or some of the lunch sandwiches in Chapter 8.

Pizza Bianca by Hand, in Pictures

1 Whisk together the flour, sugar, and salt.
2 Separately, whisk together the water and biga.
3 Cover the dough as it rises.
4 When large and bubbly, divide the dough and shape each half into a ball.
5 The rounds will spread outward. Brush the centers with olive oil and drizzle with coarse salt.
6 Dock the dough, transfer it to the peel, and gently stretch it out.
7 Dock again.
8 Brush the hot pizzas with olive oil and serve.

Naturally leavened Tuscan bread.

PANE TOSCANO

Tuscan bread

(This recipe requires the stiff starter, or biga, on page 51.)

The classic bread of Tuscany contains little or no salt. I prefer it with a pinch for two reasons: (1) it tastes better; (2) there is a curious inverse relationship between a pinch of salt and the taste of wheat. It has the paradoxical effect of helping the flavor of the wheat almost jump out of the loaf—it is a phenomenon not realized in doughs with higher levels of salt, where the salt helps the bread taste great but in the process masks, rather than enhances, the mild, subtle, ephemeral aromas of the grain. The toasty, wheaten flavors of a barely salted Tuscan loaf are unforgettable; the delicate cereal flavor of the wheat perfumes the loaf and concentrates in the crust.

This is the perfect dough for practicing your dough-handling techniques. With less salt the dough needs less water, and it is relatively firm to the touch compared to the many wetter doughs in this book. It has an enjoyable plasticity, and it is fun to shape. I am also perhaps sentimentally attached to Tuscan bread because it is the first bread I learned to make in Italy.

In a little town called Castel San Gimignano, a man named Anchiese taught me how he made it. Anchiese was a third- or fourth-generation baker with a tiny bakery down a back alleyway. Everyone from the older generation in the region said that he made the most "authentic" Tuscan bread in both texture and appearance; it was, they said, like the bread of their childhood, before the war. At the time, Anchiese was in his seventies and I was about twenty-three. It was agreed that for a short while I could go into his store at four in the morning to help him bake. When I arrived, we joked around a bit, and then he did what I eventually learned all bakers do when someone comes to help: he gave me a broom.

I spent the early mornings sweeping while he worked. I'd ask questions, and he'd talk about the dough. He measured everything by eye: a few buckets of flour, a few more of water, a fistful of salt, a big hunk of biga. He moved with the efficient but relaxed speed of someone who had been going through the same routine since he was a child. When the dough was ready, we shaped it on the windowsill. We set the loaves to leaven in beds of linen while along the window in front of us the sun rose over the Tuscan hills. To me, it was terrifically poetic and I wondered at how he could work amid such beauty. To him, it was, "*Eh, si lavora!*"—which I would translate now as, "You just work, kid."

At one point in time bakers served an essential social function—the whole community depended on the baker for its daily bread—and the job he had inherited was as much about taking care of his neighbors as it was about baking great bread.

(CONTINUES)

YIELD: One 8-inch round loaf; 1¼ pounds
EQUIPMENT: A 4½- to 5½-quart heavy pot with a tight-fitting lid; a 14-inch square of parchment paper

270 grams (1 cup plus 2 tablespoons and 1 teaspoon) water

75 grams biga (page 51)

400 grams (2¾ cups) unbleached all-purpose flour, plus flour for dusting

1.5 grams (½ teaspoon) fast-acting/instant yeast

3 grams (½ teaspoon) fine sea salt

1. Whisk the flour, yeast, and salt together in a 2-quart bowl to combine. Whisk the water and biga together in a small bowl until the biga is dissolved. Add the water and biga mixture to the flour. Use a large spoon to mix everything together very quickly until just barely combined. Cover loosely with a tea towel or a large plate and let the dough rest for 20 minutes at room temperature.

2. Dust your hands and the edges of the dough with a small handful of flour. Using a dough scraper, gently fold the edges of the dough into the middle of the dough. Turn the dough over. Cover the bowl again and allow the dough to ferment at room temperature for approximately 4 to 5 hours.

3. When the dough has doubled in size, it is ready to shape. The surface will have a glassy sheen. You will see big bubbles forming under the surface of the dough, and when you gently poke at it and gently tug at a tiny piece of it with your fingertip, it will stick to your finger and form a short, tacky strand and then spring back toward the rest of the dough when you release it. If the dough does not exhibit these properties, cover the dough and wait longer, about 30 minutes, until it does.

4. Lightly flour your hands and dust the edges of the dough with flour. Using your hands and a dough scraper, gently separate the dough from the sides of the bowl. Taking care that the dough does not tear, fold the edges of the dough into the middle. Carefully scrape the dough off the bottom of the bowl, turn it over, and cover. Wait 20 minutes or until the dough begins to grow again—you will see bubbles forming and the dough expanding just a bit.

Note on fermentation: You may notice that the proportions of flour and water in this dough are nearly identical to that of a biga—the dough will behave very much like a biga as a result. For the first 2 or 3 hours the dough may appear completely immobile. Once the fermentation reaches a certain point, though, it will grow quite quickly. It will grow more in the last 1½ hours of fermentation than it does in the first 3.

(CONTINUES)

Tuscan Bread, in Pictures

1 Whisk the flour, yeast, and salt to combine.

2 Mix the water and biga together in a separate bowl.

3 Add the water and biga to the flour.

4 Mix quickly.

5 Stop when just combined.

6 When the dough has doubled, it is ready to shape.

7 Unscored, the dough will burst open in a pretty, rustic pattern.

8 The crust will be quite thick and golden from the long, low-temperature bake.

5. Place a 14-inch square of parchment paper on a sheet pan and cover with flour: take flour by the handful and sprinkle or sift it onto the paper. You want to put enough flour down that you can no longer see the paper—and you want to avoid touching the paper with your hands to "even out" the flour; this tends to have the opposite effect.

6. Using a dough scraper, fold the edges of the dough into the center of the dough and gently pick it up. Shape it into a ball by holding it with both hands and gently tugging the sides down and under, into the middle of the dough, with the goal of making the dough into an even, taut ball. Put the dough seam side down on the floured paper. Lightly flour the dough, cover with a tea towel, and let the dough sit at room temperature until doubled in size, approximately 2 to 3 hours. The dough is ready to bake when you lightly poke a finger into it and the impression clearly remains. Place a heavy pot and a tight-fitting lid side by side on the middle rack of the oven and heat it to 380°F. Use oven mitts to take out the pot. Gently pick up the loaf and lower it into the pot with or without the parchment. Use oven mitts to cover the pot immediately and put it in the oven.

> **Beginning bakers who are nervous about picking up the dough** and lowering it into a hot pot may find it easier to simply lift up the parchment, with the dough on it, and lower both into the pot. It is okay to bake the parchment in the oven, although it may scorch. If you feel comfortable handling the dough, you might omit the parchment altogether.

7. Bake for 55 to 60 minutes, leaving the lid on the entire time. The finished bread should have a beautiful thick crust, colored a light golden brown. Remove the bread from the pot and place on a wire rack to cool.

> **Note:** This bread bakes at a much lower temperature than I usually prefer. I tend to bake bread in the manner of southern Italy—for a short period of time in an extremely hot oven, until the crust is very dark. In contrast, bakers in the northern parts of Italy, such as Tuscany, often bake breads for a longer time in a much cooler oven and in the process get a completely different sort of crust. Could you bake this bread at a higher temperature for less time, in the manner of southern Italian baking? Of course! But then it wouldn't really be Tuscan bread. Baking this low and slow gives the outside the gorgeous golden crust that (in addition to the curious lack of salt) is one of the hallmarks of Tuscan bread.

* eating

Some say Tuscan bread is made for salty things—olives, cured meats, and salty cheeses like pecorino Toscano. A competing narrative has it that Tuscan bread is simply a legacy of the notoriously stubborn Tuscan mind-set—in medieval times, landlocked Tuscans refused to pay a tax levied on salt by their seafaring neighbors. In modern times, Tuscans still refuse to give up their idiosyncratic bread. Either way, Tuscan bread is a great friend to salty foods. But because of the lovely wheat flavors, my own favorite way to eat it is to savor the delicate wheaten aromas with unsalted butter and plum jam.

PANE PUGLIESE

Pugliese-style bread

(This recipe requires the stiff starter, or biga, on page 51, and can be "kneaded" in a stand mixer.)

In the early 1990s, it was the fashion in most of northern Italy to make bread in the style of the city of Rome. But many of the bakers in the North seemed to have their roots in the South of Italy, which has quite different baking customs. In Rome I worked with many older bakers from the island of Sicily and the southeastern region of Puglia.

The bakers from Puglia, in particular, spoke of nothing with as much longing as the bread of their youth. As if describing a paradise lost, they told of an oblong loaf, simply scored, made from extremely wet dough, and baked quickly in a blazing-hot oven until the crust was nearly ½ centimeter thick. The inside of the bread, they would say, making circles with their fingers, had huge *occhi*, or eyes, throughout.

They spoke of it so often and with such reverence that I came to long for it too. When I opened Sullivan Street Bakery in 1994, I was a convert to the religion of *pane Pugliese*. I felt that I had to make it. But I had never been to Puglia!

So let me confess that this is not a centuries-old, time-honored recipe for pane Pugliese. I had heard about this bread so many times that I felt I simply knew how to make it. I think of it now as an homage to the bread described by my old baking companions.

My Pugliese dough feels much like ciabatta dough. It is quite different technically, though—it is not quite as wet as ciabatta dough, and it has much more biga in it. It is amazing how much these two factors change the finished flavor profile. Although the doughs appear similar, the finished breads look and taste completely different. The Pugliese has a pleasant touch of acidity because of the extra biga, and since it is a bit drier, it can be shaped into a round. Baking this loaf uncovered for a long period of time gives it a very dark crust with deep, seductive, slightly tart caramel flavors. It is beautifully chewy on the inside and a bit crunchy on the outside and simply gorgeous as a whole. It is exactly what you want to eat with a wonderful red wine, perhaps a Primitivo—the full-bodied wine of Puglia—or a very young pecorino cheese such as Marzolino, made in Tuscany from the earliest spring sheep's milk.

YIELD: One 9-inch round loaf; 1¼ pounds
EQUIPMENT: A 4½- to 5½-quart heavy pot with a tight-fitting lid; a 14-inch square of parchment paper

(CONTINUES)

Pugliese loaf.

295 grams (2 cups minus 1 teaspoon) unbleached all-purpose flour, plus flour for dusting

8 grams (1⅛ teaspoons) fine sea salt

1 gram (⅓ teaspoon) fast-acting/instant yeast

5 grams (1 heaping tablespoon) wheat bran

1 tablespoon extra virgin olive oil for method 2

250 grams (1 cup plus 1 tablespoon) room temperature (65° to 70°F) water

75 grams biga (page 51)

METHOD 1: BY HAND

> **Note:** If you have the time, it is worth mixing the dough by hand once or twice—I find that it is quite magical to watch the gradual transformation of the dough from a sticky mess to a supple, tacky blob of dough. If possible, give the dough a turn as described in step 2 every ½ hour or so.

1. Whisk the flour, salt, wheat bran, and yeast in a small bowl to combine. Whisk the water and biga in a 2-quart bowl until the biga is fully dissolved. Pour the dry ingredients into the water and biga mixture and use a rubber spatula to mix quickly until a wet, stringy dough forms. Do not overmix. Cover and let rest at room temperature for 20 minutes.

2. Dust the dough with flour around the edges of the bowl and use a dough scraper or well-floured hands to gently separate the dough from the sides of the bowl and fold it into the middle. Gently scrape the dough loose and flip it over. Cover the bowl and let rise at room temperature for 6 to 8 hours, until the dough triples. It will be a bit tacky, *very* stretchy, somewhat wobbly, and will feel supple to the touch when ready to shape. It should peel away cleanly from the sides of the bowl and you ought to see a few ½-inch or 1-inch bubbles at the surface.

3. Dust a work surface with flour and line a sheet pan with a 14-inch square of parchment paper. Dust the paper with wheat bran. Flour your hands and turn the dough out onto the work surface. Gently pat down the dough. Fold the corners into the center, flip over, lift up and quickly and firmly tuck it into a taut ball by pulling the edges under and into the bottom, using extra flour when necessary. This is not a cooperative dough to hold and to handle; you need to keep your hands moving so that the dough doesn't ooze and your hands don't stick. You don't need to create a perfect ball; the expanding dough will tend to correct imperfections as it rises. Set the ball down on the wheat bran seam side down. Dust the top of the loaf with a bit of flour and cover loosely with a tea towel. Allow the dough to proof at room temperature until doubled in size, 1 to 3 hours.

4. A bit before your loaf has fully leavened, put a heavy pot and a tight-fitting lid side by side on the middle rack of the oven and heat to 500°F. Use oven mitts to carefully remove the pot

from the oven. Uncover the dough and, using the paper, gently lift and lower the loaf into the pot (with or without the paper). Quickly score with a small sharp serrated knife—four lines to make a square—and cover. (Don't waste even a second—the key to a crusty crust is to capture the escaping steam in the pot as quickly as possible.) Bake, covered, for 15 minutes, uncover, remove the paper, and bake for 15 minutes more. Remove the bread from the pot and let it cool on a wire rack.

> **Note:** I like to bake this bread until the crust is, at the very least, a deep chestnut color. Letting it go even a bit further, and baking until it begins to just barely blacken in spots is fine too—if you like dark crusts (as I do!).

METHOD 2: WITH A STAND MIXER

1. In a medium bowl, stir together the flour, wheat bran, and yeast. Set aside. Lightly oil a large bowl with the olive oil and set aside. Fit a stand mixer with the pastry paddle/flat beater. Mix the water and biga on medium speed until the biga has mostly dissolved and appears frothy and well aerated. Stop the mixer and add the flour mixture. Mix on medium-low speed for about 10 seconds, until everything just comes together. Turn to maximum speed and mix for approximately 4 minutes. You will notice after a minute or two that the dough—which began in a shaggy, clumpy heap—has turned into a smooth, uniform dough that the paddle is now beginning to pull into viscous, elastic strands. When the center of the dough begins to look like a fast-moving web, stop the mixer. The dough ought to look smooth and shiny and should feel soft and warm to the touch from the intensive mixing. Add the salt and scrape down the sides of the bowl with a rubber spatula. Return the mixer to the highest speed and mix for 1 to 3 more minutes so that the salt has a chance to fully dissolve into the dough.

2. Sometimes the dough will suddenly make a thudding noise and wrap itself completely around the paddle. If it does this, it's done! Stop mixing, peel the dough off the paddle, and pour it into the oiled bowl. If the dough does not ball up around the paddle, simply stop mixing after 3 minutes and scrape the dough into the lightly oiled bowl. You will find that the dough is now incredibly viscous. It will stretch beautifully, forming long, tacky ribbons that will extend 2 to 3 feet in length before they snap. Scrape all the dough into the oiled bowl, cover loosely, and wait approximately 3 to 4 hours until it has tripled in size, is visibly bubbling, and is wonderfully wobbly. Proceed with step 3 in method 1.

Why I Love Dark Crusts

I am often accused of overbaking my bread and delivering "charred" loaves. "It's burnt," some say. But it's not. A crust can be very dark, even black—and not yet be burnt. Why argue the

(CONTINUES)

Pane Pugliese with a Stand Mixer, in Pictures

1 Weigh out ingredients.

2 Dissolve the biga into the water.

3 It should appear frothy and well aerated.

4 Add the bowl of flour, mix on low until just combined, and then switch to the highest speed.

5 After 4 minutes or so, the dough will become smooth, shiny, and stretchy.

6 Stop the mixer, add the salt, and scrape down the sides of the bowl.

7 Mix on high for a few more minutes, or until the dough wraps around the paddle.

8 Transfer the dough to an oiled container, and wait until it has tripled in size.

9 Turn the dough out onto a well-floured surface.

10 Pat down the dough and fold one corner into the center.

11 Repeat with the other corners, then flip and lift the dough and pull quickly into a ball.

12 When the loaf has risen, remove the hot pot from the preheated oven.

13 Transfer the dough to the hot pot.

14 Quickly score the loaf.

15 Quickly cover the pot.

16 Bake until the crust is beautifully colored, removing the lid and parchment halfway through.

point? Because a crust that is burnt tastes bitter. It is awful and inedible, and I don't recommend it. But a crust that is browned and darkened, perhaps already black, and almost burnt is like an intoxicating blend of dark caramel, chocolate, coffee, and maple syrup. Especially when the interior of the bread is delicate and perfumed and airy—the contrast with a sweet, dark, and truly crusty exterior is simply exquisite.

VARIATION

SESAMO
sesame seed bread

A classic Italian-American loaf of bread has sesame seeds brushed on top. It's good, but I had to take it further. My own sesame loaf is oval and coated (over, under, and on the sides) with unhulled sesame seeds. As the bread bakes, the seeds gently toast and their captivating aroma perfumes the entire loaf. The fragrance of this bread baking is one of the loveliest scents in my bakery.

YIELD: One 9-inch round loaf; 1¼ pounds   EQUIPMENT: A 4½- to 5½-quart heavy pot with a tight-fitting lid

Pane Pugliese dough (page 76)

150 grams (1 cup) unhulled sesame seeds

Mix dough for Pane Pugliese through step 3 (either method), replacing the wheat bran in step 3 with ½ cup sesame seeds, so that the shaped dough rests on a bed of sesame seeds. Use a brush or very damp towel to gently wet the dough. Sprinkle the remaining ½ cup sesame seeds over the top and sides of the dough. The seeds will act as insulation so you do not need to cover the dough. Allow the dough to proof at room temperature until it is nearly doubled in size, about 1½ hours. Heat the oven to 500°F with a pot and lid inside. Gently lift and lower the dough into the pot (with or without the paper). Score with two long slashes using a serrated knife to make an X. Bake, covered, for 20 to 25 minutes, uncover, and bake for 15 minutes, until the crust has browned and the seeds are deeply toasted. Remove the bread from the pot and let it cool on a wire rack.

✳ eating

I like to toast a slice of sesame bread and eat it with a smear of fresh, room-temperature chevre, a slice of tomato, extra virgin olive oil, and a sprinkling of fresh thyme and coarse salt.

Sesame seed loaf, shaped as an oval.

Ciabatta.

CIABATTA

open, airy slipper loaves

(This recipe requires the stiff starter, or biga, on page 51, and can be "kneaded" in a stand mixer.)

Like pane Toscano, ciabatta is a bread from northern Italy with a golden crust. But its personality couldn't be more different. Tuscan dough is as pliable as softened modeling clay. It is firm, calm, and reserved. Ciabatta dough is phenomenally wet, wobbly, and outgoing. It bubbles enthusiastically in a kind of mute hysteria. It has the solidity of a wet cloud. The dough is heavy with moisture but full of air, and it will slip away teasingly between your fingers. It is impossible to shape, but luckily . . . you don't have to! If you can resist the urge to fiddle with it, and simply pick it up and put in down in a hot pot, the ciabatta will shape itself.

This wild dough turns into a crispy loaf whose outside is rough and crackly and whose soft interior is an astounding combination of air, light, and beauty. Like the shocking heights and flying buttresses of a medieval cathedral, the structural aspects of ciabatta are in equal portions doubtful and magnificent. Can any bread have so many holes and still stand up? Yes . . . but it is hard to believe it even as you see it. Is there enough left to chew and slice? Yes! Is the texture of the crumb as glassy and unbelievably soft as it appears? Yes. Do its heavenly aspirations doom its terrestrial reality? Probably; this bread will disappear while you marvel at its existence.

This recipe makes two loaves, so, plan on baking the loaves in two pots or one right after the other, making sure the oven and the pot have recovered to a full 500°F before baking the second loaf. (These are small loaves, so you do not need a special-size pot to bake them.)

When you first lower the dough down in the pot, you may think to yourself, This looks bad. And it will. But wait! As it bakes, the craggy ravines of this messy, unshaped dough will turn into the classic ciabatta crust patterns. The finished surface will look almost like the inside of a log or the bark of a tree—long lines and whorls and textures. It's quite beautiful.

YIELD: Two 10- to 12-inch-long oblong loaves
EQUIPMENT: One or two 4½- to 5½-quart heavy pots with tight-fitting lids

300 grams (2 cups) unbleached all-purpose flour, plus flour for dusting

2 grams (⅔ teaspoon) fast-acting/instant yeast

7 grams (1 teaspoon) fine sea salt

280 grams (1¼ cups) room-temperature (65° to 70°F) water

50 grams biga (page 51)

(CONTINUES)

METHOD 1: BY HAND

1. Whisk the flour, salt, and yeast in a small bowl to combine. Whisk the water and the biga in a 3-quart bowl until the biga is fully dissolved. Pour the flour mixture into the water and biga and use a flexible spatula to mix swiftly into a sloppy dough. Stop when just combined. It is essential to stop mixing the second the dough comes together into a shaggy tangle. Overmixing this dough, even with a few extra stirs, can lead to dense, tough final loaves. Cover the bowl loosely with a tea towel and let the dough rest at room temperature for 20 minutes.

2. Dust flour around the edges of the dough and use a plastic dough scraper or well-floured hand to gently separate the dough from the bowl. Fold the edges of the dough into the center. If you have time, very gingerly turn the dough every 20 or 30 minutes two or three more times. This will speed up the process and improve the texture of the dough. It is important to do this extremely cautiously, though, so as not to deflate the delicate structure of the growing dough. Cover the bowl and allow the dough to rise at room temperature for 4 to 6 hours—or less if turned frequently. It is ready when it roils with large (½- to 1-inch-wide) bubbles, has grown by about 40 percent, and is, while sticky, also bouncy and fantastically wobbly when poked or shaken—a bit like a loose Jell-O. It should come away cleanly from the sides of the bowl when pulled.

3. Heavily flour a work surface and then apply a phenomenal amount of flour (about ½ inch deep) to a *separate* large work surface or two sheet pans on which the dough will eventually rest. Turn the dough out onto the first work surface. Fold it in half. Use a dough scraper or large knife to cut it in half (each half should weigh about 315 grams or 1¼ pounds). Without shaping them, very gently place the two pieces of dough on the heavily floured resting surface or sheet pans at least 4 inches apart. Lightly dust the tops of the loaves with flour. If the ambient environment does not feel humid, cover the doughs with a tea towel. Allow the doughs to sit at room temperature and proof until nearly doubled in size and inflated with bubbles—1 to 2 hours.

4. If you have two heavy pots and lids in which to bake the bread, put them both in the oven on the middle rack and heat to 500°F. (If you have only one pot, bake the breads one after the other.)

5. Organize your workspace so that when the oven is at temperature you will be able to pull the hot pot out of the oven and put it very near the ciabatta dough (or vice versa). When you pick up the dough, it will ooze everywhere. You will want to play hot potato and have your hot pot inches away, so that you can quickly scoop up the dough and put it down in the pot. Also consider that you want to physically handle this dough as little as possible. It ought to be

(CONTINUES)

No-Knead Ciabatta by Hand, in Pictures

1 Combine and whisk the water and biga.
2 Add the flour mixture and mix swiftly; stop when barely combined.
3 After 20 minutes, gently fold the edges of the dough into the center.
4 When ready to shape, the dough will appear extremely large and wobbly.
5 Turn the dough out onto a well-floured surface and fold in half.
6 Cut the dough in half and *without shaping* deposit each half onto a deeply floured work surface.
7 When the dough has grown and is starting to bubble, it's ready to bake.
8 Pick up the dough, stretch it the length of the pot, flip it over, and set it down. Cover quickly and bake.

bubbly and expansive and absolutely full of gas as you put it in the oven. Touching or moving it any more than is strictly necessary will deflate it.

6. When the oven is hot, take out the pot and the lid and set them down separately, near the ciabatta dough. Flour your hands, and in one smooth, quick movement, put a hand at either end of the dough, pick it up, and stretch it the length of the pot; as you lay it down in the pot flip the dough over so the well-floured bottom is on top. It ought to look awful. Cover immediately and bake for 20 to 25 minutes. The finished color should be a light, golden brown. Cool the loaves on a wire rack.

METHOD 2: WITH STAND MIXER AND PASTRY PADDLE

1. Fit a stand mixer with the pastry paddle. On medium speed, mix together the water and biga until the biga is broken up. Stop the mixer and add the flour and yeast. Mix on low speed until the ingredients blend together, then increase the speed to medium until they begin to combine—about 20 or 30 seconds. Turn the mixer to the highest speed and mix for about 3 or 4 minutes or until the dough forms viscous, elastic strands.

2. Slow the mixer, add the salt, and return to high speed. Within about 30 seconds the texture of the dough will change slightly. It will begin to stick to the paddle. Continue mixing for 1 or 2 minutes, still on high speed. The dough may come up and off the sides of the bowl and cling to the paddle. If it does, stop—it's done! Or it may stay in the bowl throughout—this is also fine; if that is the case, simply stop at the end of these 2 minutes.

3. Transfer the dough to the lightly oiled bowl and cover. Wait until the dough has more than doubled in volume, is clearly full of large bubbles, and is terrifically wobbly and bouncy when poked or jostled—2 to 3 hours. Proceed with step 3 in method 1.

✳ eating

Ciabatta lends itself to mozzarella—especially if you can find buffalo mozzarella or an extremely fresh cow's milk mozzarella. Slice the ciabatta lengthwise and fill it with a thin layer of room-temperature mozzarella, a slice of salty prosciutto, and a few fresh basil leaves if you have them.

PANE BIANCO

simple no-knead white sourdough

(This recipe requires the stiff starter, or biga, on page 51.)

For me this is the archetype of rustic country sourdough baking. It is dark and crusty on the outside, soft and open on the inside. It is straightforward, simple, and delicious. And it is easy to learn from. When I was first learning to bake with natural leavening, I'd make this dough over and over and over, trying to understand how it worked. (With no added yeast, the rise of this loaf is completely dependent on the biga.) I recommend making this bread as many times as you can. Each time you do, you will get better and you will gain more confidence and have a better idea of what to look for at each stage—after doing it a few times you may feel like an expert; after five or six times it may become addictive. You could double or triple the recipe, if you want to make enough to practice with or give away to friends. If you do multiply the recipe you could mix the doughs in separate bowls or you could mix them in one big bowl. Note, however, that the bigger the ball of dough is, the faster it will ferment!

YIELD: One 9-inch round loaf; 1¼ pounds   EQUIPMENT: A 4½- to 5½-quart heavy pot with a tight-fitting lid

300 grams (1⅓ cups) room-temperature (65° to 70°F) water

20 grams (30 grams in winter) biga (page 51)

400 grams (2¾ cups) unbleached all-purpose flour, plus flour for dusting

8 grams (1⅛ teaspoons) fine sea salt

Wheat bran for dusting

1. Whisk the water and biga together in a 1½-quart bowl until the biga dissolves. Add the flour and, using a large spoon or spatula, rapidly and vigorously mix everything together until it is just combined—about 20 seconds. Resist the urge to tidy it or consolidate it. Scrape the dough off your spoon and from the edges of the bowl and put it on top of the dough in the bowl. Cover the bowl with a plate and let it sit at room temperature for 20 minutes. Flour the edges of the dough lightly and use a dough scraper or rubber spatula to turn the dough: fold the edges of the dough into the center. Cover again and let sit for 8 to 18 hours (the colder the weather, the longer it takes), until the dough has doubled in size and is sweet and yeasty smelling.

(CONTINUES)

Pane bianco: basic no-knead sourdough.

Readiness: Sometimes it is hard to tell when the dough has "doubled" and is ready to shape. Here are some visual and tactile markers—aside from eyeballing its volume—to help you judge its readiness to shape. When the dough is ready, it will glisten and shimmer and you will see a few bubbles beneath the surface. It should feel light, springy, and curiously soft to the touch. The dough will have a gassy feel, as if it were inflating (which it is). When you pull a strand of it up and away from the bowl, it will thin out as you pull it, so that it is nearly transparent—the classic "windowpane" test. And when it is *really* ready to shape, the dough will have developed self-suction. It will stick to things—your finger, the bowl, a rubber spatula—but when you pull away, rather than leave a mess, it will come away quickly and cleanly, with snap and enthusiasm. When the dough reaches this point of beautiful springiness, it has reached the apex of its elasticity—and it is ready to shape.

2. Flour the edges of the dough again, scrape from the side of the bowl, and fold them into the center of the dough. Scrape the dough off the bottom of the bowl and flip it over. Let the dough rest at room temperature, covered, for 20 minutes or until the dough shows signs it is growing: a slight but noticeable expansion.

3. Line a rimmed baking sheet with a tea towel or parchment paper. Grab a handful of flour or wheat bran and sprinkle it onto the tea towel to cover a large circle in the center.

On coating tea towels with flour or bran: Cover the tea towel so completely with flour or bran that the tea towel is no longer visible in a large 12-inch circle area in the center. Try not to touch the tea towel with your hands or fingers. I always advise against using your hand or fingers to try to spread out piles of flour more evenly—this is a natural impulse, but I find that it often has the opposite effect and ends up exposing bits of fabric rather than covering them, so that the dough eventually sticks to the exposed bits of fabric. Some folks prefer to sift the flour over the resting surface. Bran, though, is simpler and less messy. Plus it can be used over and over again (see page 30).

Many people prefer to rest their dough on parchment paper. This allows them to simply pick up the paper, with the dough on it, and transfer the whole bundle to the hot pot. I advise using whichever method works best for you. If you do use parchment, I advise gently extracting it when you lift the lid off the pot at the end of the baking. At very high temperatures the parchment can begin to char.

4. Imperfections are beautiful. It's always better to stop with an imperfect round than to keep pulling at it until it tears in a grim attempt to achieve perfection. With that in mind: gently fold the sides of the dough into the middle of the dough and lift the dough from the bowl. Throw a handful of flour into the bowl. Working quickly and gently, pull the dough into a taut

(CONTINUES)

ball—the tension is what will allow the dough to hold its shape. You need to work quickly so the dough doesn't stick to you. If it starts to stick, dip it in the floury bowl. Pull the sides of the dough down and into the bottom of the dough. You are trying to make the surface of the dough as taut as you can without tearing it—in about 30 seconds or less. (Handling the dough any more than this is likely to damage the airy, delicate structure within.)

5. Put the dough seam side down on the coated tea towel. Lift up the corners of the tea towel and loosely cover the dough with them or a new tea towel. Let the dough rest at room temperature 1 to 3 hours, until it has doubled in size. Place a large pot and a tight-fitting lid side by side in the oven on the middle rack and heat the oven to 500°F.

6. Use oven mitts to carefully remove the pot from the oven and uncover the dough. Very gently pick the dough up and lower it into the pot. Use a small serrated or pairing knife to score the dough with a single slash. Cover the pot immediately and bake for 40 to 45 minutes. Take the lid off (and remove the parchment, if using) and bake for 5 to 10 minutes, until the crust has attained at least a rich golden color; if you favor a really dark crust as I do, you can go as far as 12 minutes to a deep mahogany.

   When the bread comes out of the oven, you'll know it is done baking because it will feel lighter, it will sound hollow when you knock on the bottom, and the crust will soon begin to crackle quietly like logs in a fire. Set the loaf on a wire rack to cool.

   If you can bear to, wait an hour or so before cutting into it, as the interior will continue to cook as it cools.

TRUCCIO SARÉ

whole wheat sourdough

(This recipe requires the stiff starter, or biga, on page 51.)

There is a town outside of Rome called Lariano. It grows a special kind of wheat, known as Lariano wheat, and the bread made in this town uses whole wheat Lariano flour. It is a dusky gray and has a peculiar grit to it. I was told that this is because it is an ancient variety of wheat—grown on those hills since the days of the Roman Empire. I don't know whether that's true, but I have always loved the sentiment of making bread with special kinds of wheat that grow well in a particular area. When I started working with North Country Farms a few years ago, I immediately thought of Lariano. The North Country is a historic farming region in upstate New York—so far north that it borders Canada. I loved the idea of making a special bread that brought out the luscious, exquisite flavors of our own local wheat grains (which are neither gray nor gritty nor of a particularly noble pedigree). If you have the inclination, I entreat you to track down a regionally grown wheat to make this bread. You can, however, make it with ordinary whole wheat flour, and it will still have an awesome, complex, earthy flavor.

Compared to loaves made entirely with white flour, you will find this dough to be drier in texture and denser in weight. Whole wheat absorbs more water than white flour and changes the texture and flavor of the dough. I love this bread for soaking up sauce and soups, for hearty sandwiches, and for eating with soft, slightly stinky cheeses.

My absolute favorite part is the crust. At a very high temperature, when the crust browns so thoroughly that it is just beginning to blacken in places, the whole wheat begins to caramelize. The flavors that result are out of this world—a sweet, chewy tangle of wheat, coffee, dark chocolate, and caramel.

What's in a name? Well, this one I made up. There is a line of baked goods in Italy called Mulino Bianco—it's kind of like the Italian version of Nabisco. They have a huge variety of cookies and pastries, and each one has a silly name (much like Mulino Bianco itself, which means "white mill"). I have always loved these names and the imaginary sense of history and tradition they convey.

When I came up with the truccio formula a few years ago, I wanted to give it a beautiful name. I had previously sold a loaf called the casareccio—which means "homemade." I was replacing the casareccio with the new loaf, and I wanted to give customers something that sounded familiar and reliable, so I took "casareccio" and dropped the *ca*, kept the *sare* and *ccio* parts, and reversed them. I also felt that the new loaf looked a bit like a torpedo. (In the bakery, the truccio is an oblong shape.) So I added a *t* for good measure. The end product was *truccio saré*, which I hope you will agree has a nice ring to it. (It means nothing in any language that I'm aware of.)

(CONTINUES)

Truccio saré: no-knead whole wheat sourdough.

YIELD: One 9-inch round loaf; 1¼ pounds

EQUIPMENT: A 4½- to 5½-quart heavy pot with a tight-fitting lid; a 14-inch square of parchment paper

20 grams (30 grams in winter) biga (page 51)

300 grams (1⅓ cups) room-temperature (65° to 70°F) water

100 grams (⅔ cups) whole wheat flour

300 grams (2 cups) unbleached all-purpose flour

8 grams (1⅛ teaspoons) fine sea salt

Wheat bran for dusting

1. Whisk the biga and water together in a large bowl.

2. Add the wheat and white flours and the salt to the water and use a spoon or spatula (or hand—anything but a whisk, which gets stuck!) to vigorously mix all the ingredients together. Stop as soon as the flour and water come together—it should take only around 15 seconds. Scrape any dough off the spoon or your hands and drop it back into the bowl. Cover the bowl loosely with a tea towel and let it sit at room temperature for 20 minutes.

3. Turn the dough: gently lift up each side of the dough and fold it into the middle of the bowl. It should take 5 seconds or so from start to finish—this is more of a gesture than a precise technique. The goal is to move the dough; simply folding the dough on top of itself a few times is enough to speed up the fermentation and improve the texture of the finished loaf. Cover the bowl with a tea towel and let rest at room temperature for 10 to 18 hours, until it has increased in size by a third to a half.

> **Note:** If you are in a hot environment (75°F or more), be extra attentive to the growth of the dough—you do not want this dough to grow too large, because it may begin to collapse. The bran in the wheat flour cuts the gluten network and tends to decrease the ability of the dough to trap gas. This makes it especially hard for the natural leavening to raise the dough a second time.

4. When the dough is ready to shape, it will be larger, airier, and have a soft, spongy texture. You should also see bubbles under the surface of the dough. Turn the dough again: pick up the sides of the dough, fold them gently into the middle, and flip the dough over. Cover the bowl with a tea towel and wait 20 minutes or until the dough shows signs that it is beginning to grow again—a bubble or two or a slight overall expansion.

5. Place a 14-inch square of parchment paper on a sheet pan and dust with wheat bran. You want to put enough bran down that you can no longer see the paper.

(CONTINUES)

6. Using a dough scraper or your hands, fold the edges of the dough into the center and gently pick it up. Shape it into a ball by holding it with both hands and gently tugging the sides down and under, into the middle of the dough, with the goal of making the dough into a nice, taut ball. Take care to stop before the dough begins to tear. You want to create enough tension in your ball of dough that it will hold its shape as it proofs, but not so much tension that the exterior of the dough rips or snags. Put the dough seam side down on the bran-coated paper.

7. Dust the top of the dough lightly with more bran. Cover it loosely with a tea towel. Let the dough sit at room temperature until it has doubled in size, 2 to 4 hours. Once the dough has nearly doubled, put a rack in the center of the oven. Put a heavy pot and tight-fitting lid side by side in the oven and heat to 450°F. Use oven mitts to carefully remove the pot and lid. Lift the dough on the parchment up and lower it into the pot. Use a serrated or sharp paring knife to score the loaf with one ¼- to ½-inch slash. Cover the pot immediately and place the pot in the oven.

8. Bake for 35 to 40 minutes with the lid on. Carefully remove the lid and bake for another 10 to 15 minutes, until the crust is a very, very dark brown. On account of the higher mineral and fiber content in whole wheat flour, the crust will naturally be much darker than that of breads made solely with white flour, even before it is fully done. As a result, when you first take the lid off the pot, the crust may be so brown already that it appears to be done. It is not. Taking the bread out now will yield a soft and squishy crust. I urge you to let the bread cook, uncovered, until the top of the bread nearly blackens and the sides reach a shockingly dark brown—the flavors of such a well-done truccio crust are simply outstanding. Remove the loaf from the pot. Cool the loaf on a wire rack. The loaf will continue to cook as it cools, so try to wait an hour or so before cutting into it.

✳ eating

When I am at home in the kitchen, surveying the landscape and wondering what to make for dinner, I often decide the process will go more smoothly with a slice of truccio in hand. Toasted, dripping with olive oil and red wine vinegar, and dusted with a bit of salt, it's messy and delicious and is the most wonderful way to begin a meal.

The malty, chocolaty notes of the crust also make this bread the best friend of wines, jams, and soft-ripened cheeses, whether classics like Camembert or Brie or something made closer to home.

FASTER TRUCCIO

whole wheat sourdough
(This recipe requires an extremely fresh stiff starter, or biga, on page 51.)

Often I counsel patience when baking—so very often, the only secret to making a good bread better is to wait a bit longer and let the flavors, fermentation, and rise develop. But I am also an impatient guy, and there are times when I want to mix, bake, and eat a loaf not tomorrow but today. Here is a recipe for those moments. It's not instant bread, but it is faster bread. This recipe has a larger amount of biga than most. Be aware that the faster the fermentation, the more keen an eye you have to keep on your dough to ensure that it does not ferment too much, lose strength, and leave you with a dense, sour disk. This loaf will be around 5 inches tall with an open crumb and a honeycombed interior of dime- to quarter-size holes.

YIELD: One 9-inch round loaf; 1¼ pounds
EQUIPMENT: A 4½- to 5½-quart heavy pot with a tight-fitting lid; a 14-inch square of parchment paper

200 grams (1¼ cups plus 2 tablespoons) unbleached all-purpose flour

100 grams (⅔ cup) whole wheat flour

6 grams (1 teaspoon) fine sea salt

100 grams extremely fresh (see page 28) biga (page 51)

250 grams (1 cup plus 1 tablespoon) room-temperature (65° to 70°F) water

Wheat bran for dusting

1. Whisk the white flour, wheat flour, and salt in a large bowl to combine. Whisk the biga and water in a small bowl until the biga is fully dissolved. Pour the water and biga mixture into the flour and use a flexible spatula to mix quickly. Cover the bowl loosely with a tea towel and let the dough sit at room temperature for 20 minutes.

2. Every half hour, turn the dough: with lightly floured hands and a dough scraper, pull the dough off the sides of the bowl, fold it into the center, and turn the dough over. Cover loosely with a tea towel in between turns. After approximately six turns, or 3 hours, the dough should be ready. Don't expect to see a big increase in size in this dough; by turning the dough every half hour, you are doing what I call the lazy man's version of kneading the dough—improving the texture without much effort. You are also knocking the air out of the dough with every turn. This is a practical process because the agitation involved in turning and folding the dough also speeds up the fermentation so that those deflated bubbles quickly fill up again.

(CONTINUES)

Note: How do you tell when it's ready? You want it to get to the point where it is capable of holding a shape and not ooze into a pancake when you shape it into a ball. So you want to make sure the dough is going to be extremely elastic—it should do such a good job of sticking to itself that it will easily peel off the bowl when it's ready to shape. Pull up a bit of the dough to see if it stretches easily. If it does, and thins out to a transparent, "windowpane"-like state, it's ready.

3. Place a 14-inch square of parchment paper on a sheet pan and cover with wheat bran. You want to put enough bran down that you can no longer see the paper.

4. Using a dough scraper or your hands, fold the edges of the dough into the center of the dough and gently pick it up. Shape it into a ball by holding it with both hands and gently tugging the sides down and under, into the middle of the dough, with the goal of making the dough into a taut ball. Take care to stop before the dough begins to tear. You want to create enough tension in your ball of dough that it will hold its shape as it proofs, but not so much tension that the exterior of the dough rips or snags. Put the dough seam side down on the bran-coated paper.

5. Dust the top of the dough lightly with more bran. Cover it loosely with a tea towel and let it sit at room temperature until it has doubled in size, 1½ to 3 hours, and looks and feels as if it is inflating. Once the dough has nearly doubled, put a heavy pot and tight-fitting lid side by side into the oven and heat to 450°F. Use oven mitts to carefully remove the pot and lid. Lift the dough on the parchment and lower it into the pot. Use a serrated or sharp paring knife to score the loaf with a triangle shape. Cover the pot immediately and place the pot in the oven.

6. Bake for 35 to 40 minutes with the lid on. Carefully remove the lid and bake for another 10 to 15 minutes, until the crust is a very, very dark brown. On account of the higher mineral and fiber content in the whole wheat, the crust of this bread will naturally be much darker than that of breads made solely with white flour, even before it is fully done. As a result, when you first take the lid off the pot, the crust may be so brown already that it appears to be done. It is not. I urge you to let the bread cook, uncovered, until the top of the bread nearly blackens and the sides reach a very dark brown. Remove the loaf from the pot. Cool the loaf on a wire rack. The loaf will continue to cook as it cools, so try to wait an hour or so before cutting into it.

MULTIGRANI

seed and grain bread
(This recipe requires the stiff starter, or biga, on page 51.)

This nutty, seedy, earthy brown bread is now a universal favorite at Sullivan Street Bakery. But it didn't start out that way. There was a German baker working at the bakery who insisted on making a many-seeded loaf in the tradition of many northeastern European breads. I was unenthusiastic, to say the least. I do like the occasional dense rye loaf and all those northern European breads full of seeds, but it just wasn't what I wanted to make at the bakery, which I have always imagined as Italian in inspiration. But everyone loved this bread so much I felt I couldn't say no, and now I love it too. It is aromatic, a little bit sweet, deliciously chewy, not at all dense, and rather porous. It goes beautifully with hard cheeses such as Gruyère and Piave, and it makes spectacular toast. I think of it as I would an unusual but strangely familiar piece of art—it's a German desire expressing itself in an Italianate form.

Before this bread is mixed, a mixture of grains and seeds is softened in hot water. Incidentally, this mixture also makes a delectable breakfast porridge. I have been known to remake this portion of the seed mix after tasting and eating the entire bowl of cooling seeds.

YIELD: One 9-inch round loaf; 1¼ pounds
EQUIPMENT: A 4½- to 5½-quart heavy pot with a tight-fitting lid, a 14-inch square of parchment paper

FOR THE SOAKER:

40 grams (¼ cup) barley

40 grams (scant ½ cup) rolled oats

20 grams (2 tablespoons) flax seeds

20 grams (2 tablespoons) sesame seeds

20 grams (2 tablespoons) sunflower seeds

20 grams (1 tablespoon plus 2 teaspoons) millet

330 grams (1 cup plus 2 tablespoons) water

FOR THE BREAD:

250 grams (1½ cups) unbleached all-purpose flour, plus flour for dusting

50 grams (⅓ cup plus 1 tablespoon) whole wheat flour

20 grams (2 tablespoons) whole or white rye flour

7 grams (1 teaspoon) fine sea salt

10 grams (30 grams in winter) biga (page 51)

80 grams (⅓ cup plus 1 teaspoon) room-temperature (65° to 70°F) water

5 grams (1 teaspoon) honey

Wheat bran for dusting

Olive oil for the bowl

(CONTINUES)

1. Put the barley, oats, flax, sesame, sunflower, and millet seeds into a small bowl. Remove 40 grams (¼ cup) and set aside. Bring 250 grams (1 cup and 2 tablespoons) of water to a boil in a small saucepan. Immediately pour over the bowl of grains. Mix gently and set aside for an hour or so, until the warm seeds, also known as "the soaker," are warm, not hot, to the touch.

2. Put the white, whole wheat, and rye flours in a medium bowl with the salt. Put the biga, water, and honey in a larger bowl and whisk until the biga dissolves. Stir in the cooled soaker. Add the dry ingredients and quickly mix together until just combined. Cover loosely and let rest at room temperature for 20 minutes. Dust the edges of the dough with flour and use a dough scraper to gently fold the edges of the dough into the center. Flip the dough over and transfer to a lightly oiled bowl to ferment. Cover it loosely with a tea towel and let the dough ferment at room temperature for 8 to 11 hours, until nearly doubled in size, soft to the touch, and dome shaped on top.

3. Lightly dust flour around the edges of the dough and use your hands to gently peel the dough away from the sides and bottom of the bowl. Pick up the sides of the dough and fold them into the center of the dough. Re-cover and allow to rest at room temperature for 20 minutes.

4. Put a 14-inch square of parchment paper on a sheet pan and dust it with wheat bran and 10 grams (1 tablespoon) of the reserved dry seeds. Turn the dough out onto a heavily floured work surface and shape into a ball by gently folding the edges into the center—the rye flour in this dough requires gentle handling, so this is all the shaping this loaf requires. Place the dough seam side down on top of the seeded paper. Give the dough a light coating of water with a pastry brush and sprinkle the remaining 30 grams (3 tablespoons) of seeds on top of the dough. Cover the dough loosely with a tea towel and allow it to sit at room temperature until doubled in size, 1½ to 3 hours.

5. Put a large heavy pot and a tight-fitting lid side by side on a rack in the bottom third of the oven and heat the oven to 450°F. Uncover the dough. Use oven mitts to remove the pot and the lid from the oven. Using the sides of the parchment, carefully pick up and lower the dough on the paper into the pot. Use a small serrated or sharp paring knife to give the dough one long, shallow slash (less than ¼ inch deep). Quickly cover the pot and return to the oven. Bake for 40 minutes, remove the lid, and bake for 15 to 20 minutes, until the crust is a deep chestnut color and the seeds are deeply toasted. Remove from the pot and cool the loaf on a wire rack.

HAMILTON BUNS

sweet whole wheat

(This recipe requires the stiff starter, or biga, on page 51, and can be "kneaded" in a stand mixer.)

I saw *Hamilton*, the musical, in the fall of 2015. I became deeply obsessed with both the musical and the historical figure. I read Ron Chernow's biography of Alexander Hamilton, I read *The Federalist Papers*, and I developed the irritating habit of finding a way to fit Lin-Manuel Miranda's dazzling lyrics into every conversation. For Hamilton's birthday that winter, I decided I had to bake in his honor. "Hamwiches" seemed appropriate—nice little sandwiches made of ham, mustard, and pickle. I don't know what Hamilton actually ate, but this seemed like Revolutionary War–era fare to me. And of course, for a perfect hamwich, I needed a perfect bun. I imagined a diamond in the rough—a serious-sounding workhorse with surprising delicacy and flair. Here is what I came up with: a whole wheat bun of substance, character, and ample sweetness. May it amaze and astonish.

YIELD: 12 rolls   EQUIPMENT: A stand mixer with the paddle attachment, and an 18-by-13-inch rimmed sheet pan

225 grams (1½ cups) whole wheat flour

175 grams (1 cup plus 3 tablespoons) unbleached all-purpose flour, plus flour for dusting

6 grams (1 teaspoon) fine sea salt

5 grams (1½ teaspoons) fast-acting/instant yeast

Olive oil for the bowl

180 grams (¾ cup) whole milk, plus 30 grams (2 tablespoons) for brushing the buns

180 grams (¾ cup) water

40 grams (2 tablespoons) molasses

40 grams biga (page 51)

1. Put the whole wheat and white flours, the salt, and the yeast in the bowl of a stand mixer. Oil a large bowl and set aside.

2. Bring the milk to a boil in a small saucepan over medium-high heat. Remove from the heat, add the water, and set aside to cool to 70°F.

3. Add the molasses, the biga, and the cooled milk and water mixture to the bowl of flour. With the paddle attachment, mix on low for 30 seconds to combine, and then raise the speed to medium-high. After 2½ minutes, scrape down the bowl. Mix again until the dough forms a ball—it should happen quite quickly.

(CONTINUES)

Hamilton buns.

4. Transfer the dough to the oiled bowl. Cover and let rise for 45 minutes to 1 hour. Pay careful attention; the dough needs to be cut and shaped as soon as it has just about doubled, lest it rise too high to survive. It is helpful to put this dough in a walled container and make a mark on the side to judge when the dough has almost doubled in size.

5. Turn the dough out onto a lightly floured surface. Divide the dough in half, then cut each half into six pieces using a dough scraper or chef's knife. Each piece should weigh 65 to 75 grams. Shape each piece into a ball and arrange on a parchment-lined sheet pan 1½ inches apart. Cover with a damp tea towel and allow to proof at room temperature for 1 to 2 hours (but no more), or until the buns are just kissing one another. Heat the oven to 450°F. Uncover the rolls and brush lightly with milk. Bake for 15 minutes or until light brown. Allow the buns to cool on the pan.

＊ eating

Serve with country ham, homemade mustard (page 197), and thinly sliced pickles.

Chickpea fritter and tahini sandwich
(page 183) on whole wheat pita.

WHOLE WHEAT PITA BREAD

(This recipe uses the stiff starter, or biga, on page 51 as an optional ingredient, and can be "kneaded" in a stand mixer.)

Pitas cook in a completely different manner from my other breads—they are so thin that they fill with steam and inflate in the heat of the oven—and are done in a matter of minutes. I like to make these pitas with only whole wheat flour, which gives them a rich, nutty flavor.

Having the pizza stone very hot is key for getting the dough to puff up properly, and placing the pitas in a fabric-lined basket when they come out of the oven allows the pitas to cool and keeps them soft.

YIELD: Eight 6-inch round pitas   EQUIPMENT: A stand mixer with the paddle attachment and a pizza stone

Olive oil for the bowl

325 grams (1½ cups) room-temperature (65° to 70°F) water

10 grams biga (optional; page 51)

5 grams (1 teaspoon) sugar

400 grams (2¾ cups) whole wheat flour, plus flour for dusting

1 gram (⅓ teaspoon) fast-acting/instant yeast

6 grams (1 teaspoon) salt

1. Oil a medium bowl and set it aside. Dust a large sheet pan or work surface with whole wheat flour. Put the water and biga (if using) into the bowl of a stand mixer fitted with the paddle attachment. Mix on low speed for 1 minute. Add the sugar, flour, and yeast and mix on low until the ingredients are moistened. Increase the speed to medium and mix for 2 minutes. Add the salt and mix for 2 minutes. Transfer the dough to the oiled bowl. Cover with a plate or plastic wrap. Let the dough ferment at room temperature for 2 to 3 hours or until the dough has doubled in volume. Form the dough into eight equal pieces (about 60 grams each). Shape the pieces of dough into balls. Place the balls 2 inches apart on a floured surface. Cover the dough with a damp tea towel. Allow the dough to proof at room temperature for 45 minutes to 1½ hours, or until the dough balls have started to show some growth. (This also gives the dough a chance to relax and become easier to roll very thin.)

2. While the dough is proofing, place a pizza stone on the center rack of the oven. Remove any racks above the stone. Heat the oven to 500°F. (The pizza stone needs to be very hot for the pitas to puff up.) Line a large basket with a tea towel and set aside until the pitas are coming out of the oven.

(CONTINUES)

3. When ready to bake, use a rolling pin to roll the dough into very thin 6-inch circles that are about ⅛ inch thick. Let the circles rest for 5 minutes.

4. Place two pitas on the pizza stone at a time, bottom side up. Bake for 1½ minutes or until the pita puffs up. Then gingerly flip the pitas over and bake for 1 minute, or until they puff up again. Add the baked pitas to the towel-lined basket. Repeat with the remaining dough.

NO-KNEAD, NATURALLY LEAVENED BRIOCHE

a light and buttery bread
(This recipe requires an extremely fresh stiff starter, or biga, on page 51, and can be "kneaded" in a stand mixer.)

Soft, sweet, and golden, this Italian-style brioche dough is sweeter and cakier than its French cousin. Enriched with egg, butter, and honey and flavored with lemon and vanilla, the sweet smells this dough exudes as it bakes could drive one to distraction. This recipe will make one loaf, twelve small rolls, or six larger, hamburger-size rolls. Italians seem to serve sweet brioche rolls at every opportunity, and I have happily adopted this habit. I use them for everything from egg sandwiches in the morning to hamburgers in the evening. So much of the flavor and texture of this bread depends on the butter you use, so this is the time to splurge on the good stuff—I am partial to Irish butters such as Kerrygold.

When leavened the very traditional way with sourdough instead of dry baker's yeast, this dough is particularly delicate. For the fluffiest, softest version, use a stand mixer. This will also speed up the rising of the bread, enhancing the growth of yeast due to increased oxygen. Mixed by hand as a no-knead, it is still divine—but the texture is cakier. Either way, you will find that the honey and natural leavening act as natural preservatives, keeping a brioche loaf in a fine state for a week or more. It is the only one of my breads I would consider sealing in a bag or a box. It is naturally soft and moist, and—unlike the crusty breads I usually make—its integrity will not be harmed by the added moisture created by being kept sealed.

Either the hand-mixed or mixer version of this dough can be used to make Bomboloni (page 153), Cardamom Cinnamon Buns (page 147), or the Chocolate Swirl Brioche Loaf (page 150).

YIELD: One 8½-by-4½-inch loaf; 1½ pounds
EQUIPMENT: An 8½-by-4½-inch metal loaf pan if making a loaf; a sheet pan if making rolls

(CONTINUES)

Naturally leavened brioche.

100 grams (a scant ½ cup) water

113 grams (1 stick/8 tablespoons) unsalted butter

90 grams (a scant ½ cup) sugar

5 grams (1 teaspoon) honey

2 large eggs at room temperature

4 grams (1 teaspoon) vanilla extract

Very finely chopped or grated zest of ½ lemon

125 grams extremely fresh (see page 28) biga (page 51)

270 grams (1¾ cups plus 2 tablespoons) unbleached all-purpose flour, plus flour for dusting

6 grams (1 teaspoon) fine sea salt

Olive oil for the bowl

METHOD 1: IN A STAND MIXER

1. Gently heat the water, butter, sugar, and honey to a pleasantly warm temperature, about 100°F, in a small saucepan over low heat. Allow to cool a bit. Transfer to a stand mixer fitted with the paddle attachment. Mix on low speed until the sugar dissolves. Add the eggs, vanilla, and lemon zest. Add the biga and mix at medium speed until mostly dissolved. Stop the mixer, add the flour and salt, and mix on low until just combined. Mix on medium-high for 10 to 15 minutes, or until the dough ribbons, webs, and pulls off the side of the bowl.

2. Scrape off the paddle, scrape down the sides of the bowl, cover loosely with a damp tea towel, and allow to barely double in size, 6 to 9 hours at room temperature. (If you are going to need to free up the mixer, transfer to an oiled bowl and cover with a damp tea towel.) When the dough is ready, it will be soft, supple, and inflated with air.

3. Heavily flour a work surface. Line an 8½-by-4½-inch loaf pan with parchment paper, with 2 inches of paper hanging over each end. Lightly flour your hands and the edges of the dough. Use a dough scraper to gently pry the dough loose from the bowl, taking care not to tear it. Turn the dough out onto the floured work surface and pat it down firmly to flatten it. Pick up the left side of the dough and fold it two-thirds of the way toward the right side. Then pick up the right side and fold it two-thirds of the way toward the left side. Gently pat down the dough again and turn the top of the dough (the point farthest from you) into a "bike seat": fold the corners down to make a very small triangle. Pat down the tip of the triangle very firmly and then roll it toward you. Continue rolling the dough toward you until you have a neat cylinder. Put the dough seam side down in the paper-lined loaf pan and cover with a damp tea towel to keep it moist so a skin does not form on the surface of the loaf. Let the dough rise at room temperature until it reaches the top of the pan—2 to 4 hours in the summer and as many as 8 to 10 hours in the winter.

(CONTINUES)

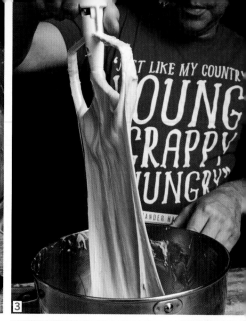

Naturally Leavened Brioche in a Stand Mixer, in Pictures

1 After mixing the first few ingredients, add the biga.

2 After adding the flour and salt, mix slowly to combine and then quickly, until the dough forms strings and webs.

3 The dough will pull into long, beautiful, elastic ribbons.

4 Once the dough has fully leavened, turn it out and firmly flatten it.

5 Fold the left side of the dough two-thirds of the way to the right, and the right side to the corners of the left side.

6 Pat down again and fold the far corners in, as if making a bike seat or paper plane. Pat down the tip of the triangle quite firmly, then gently but firmly roll it inward and toward you until you have a single chubby tube.

7 Transfer the tube to the prepared pan, stretching it out if necessary.

8 Wait for the dough to rise just above the pan.

4. Heat the oven to 375°F. Remove the damp tea towel and bake the brioche, uncovered, for 45 to 50 minutes, until the top is light brown. (If the top begins to brown too quickly, cover it with foil.) Let the loaf cool for 5 minutes and then use the parchment paper to pull the loaf from the pan. Allow to cool on a wire rack before eating.

METHOD 2: BY HAND

1. Stir the flour and salt together in a medium bowl until combined. Gently warm the water, butter, sugar, and honey to a pleasantly warm temperature, about 100°F in a small saucepan over low heat. Whisk until the butter melts and the sugar dissolves. Transfer to a large bowl and whisk the eggs and vanilla. Add to it the cooled butter and sugar mixture, whisking to incorporate. Add the biga and whisk vigorously until completely combined. Add the flour mixture and lemon zest and use a rubber spatula to mix quickly, rotating the bowl and lifting from the bottom to incorporate evenly. Stop mixing the moment a lumpy batter forms; it is important not to overmix. Cover the bowl with a damp tea towel and let rest for 20 minutes at room temperature.

2. Lightly flour the edges of the dough. Use a dough scraper or well-floured hands to scrape the batter off the sides of the bowl and into the center of the dough. Cover the bowl with a damp tea towel. Every 30 minutes, "turn" the dough using a dough scraper. To turn the dough, sprinkle a little flour around the edge of the dough and use the scraper to lift the edges of the dough up and into the center of the bowl. Repeat four times, leaving the dough covered and at room temperature between turns, for a total of 2 hours. After the final turn, let the dough ferment, covered, for 4 hours. The dough is ready to be shaped when it's nearly doubled in volume. Proceed from step 3 in method 1.

VARIATION

FOR LITTLE ROLLS OR HAMBURGER BUNS

For little rolls, when the dough is ready to shape, rather than folding it into a loaf, divide it into twelve even pieces (or six for hamburger buns), using a dough scraper (alternatively, dust two fingers with flour and pretend they are scissors—it works well and is surprisingly fun). Fold the dough under and into itself to make taut little balls, but do not handle the dough so much that the dough gets sticky—this means you're stretching too much. Put the shaped balls of dough onto a sheet pan lined with parchment paper or lightly oiled. Allow the rolls to double in volume—1½ to 3 hours in the summer, 6 to 8 hours in the winter. Heat the oven to 450°F. Once it is hot, brush the tops of the rolls with a beaten egg and bake the rolls for about 15 minutes (20 minutes for hamburger buns) or until the tops have colored.

"wastED" bread

bread from bread

(This recipe requires the stiff starter, or biga, on page 51, and can be "kneaded" in a stand mixer.)

Chef Dan Barber once held a special event at his New York City restaurant, Blue Hill. The project was called "wastED," and it was devoted to food waste "education"—specifically the fact that the U.S. Department of Agriculture estimates that 30 to 40 percent of the U.S. food supply is wasted. For two weeks the wastED team only cooked and served food that would otherwise have been discarded—vegetable trimmings, fish bones, you name it. They asked me to come up with a bread made entirely of ingredients that would otherwise have been waste. It was fascinating and educational to look around the bakery in a new way and find all the perfectly good "waste" ingredients. I ultimately came up with a bread made from stale bread that I ground into flour. The bread made from bread was unassuming in appearance with a rough, open crumb, but it was particularly well developed in flavor, with a sly undertone of maltiness, as if the flour had been toasted—which in a way it had. Here is a version of that bread for baking at home.

YIELD: Two 7-inch round loaves, ¾ pound each
EQUIPMENT: One or two 4½- to 5½-quart heavy pots with tight-fitting lids

200 grams (4 cups) stale bread ground to crumbs

300 grams (2 cups) unbleached all-purpose flour, plus flour for dusting

275 grams (1 cup plus 3 tablespoons) water

100 grams biga (page 51)

3 grams (1 teaspoon) fast-acting/instant yeast

4 grams (¾ teaspoon) fine sea salt

Olive oil for the bowl

1. Combine 50 grams (1 cup) of the bread crumbs with 50 grams (⅓ cup) of the flour in a small bowl and set aside to use for dusting.

2. Soak the remaining 150 grams (3 cups) of stale bread in the water in the bowl of a stand mixer for about an hour or until soft. Put the remaining 250 grams (1⅔ cups) of flour, the biga, and the yeast into the stand mixer bowl. With the paddle attachment, mix on low speed for 30 seconds or until all the ingredients come together. Increase the speed to medium and continue mixing for about 4 minutes, until the dough becomes smooth and elastic. As the dough begins to attach itself to the mixer, slow the mixer and add the salt. Return to medium speed and mix for 1½ minutes; the dough is done when it begins to stick to itself more than the bowl.

3. Transfer the dough to an oiled bowl, cover, and allow to ferment at room temperature until it doubles in size, approximately 2 hours. The dough will be soft, sticky, and elastic.

4. Cover a sheet pan with the flour-crumb mixture. On a well-floured surface, divide the dough in half. Shape each piece of dough into a round. Place the loaves seam side down on the crumb mixture. Cover the dough with a tea towel. Allow the dough to proof at room temperature for 2½ hours or until doubled in size.

5. If you have two heavy pots and lids and enough oven space, put both pots and lids side by side in the oven and heat to 450°F. (If you have only one pot, bake the breads one after the other.)

6. When the oven is hot, use oven mitts and take out the pot or pots and the lids and set them down separately, near the dough. Flour your hands, and lower the dough or doughs into the pot(s). Cover the pots immediately and bake for 30 minutes. Uncover and bake for 5 minutes or until the loaves are deeply browned. Cool the loaves on a wire rack.

Capicola pizza (page 121).

5

SULLIVAN STREET
PIZZA

AT THE CAFÉ WE MAKE MANY RECTANGULAR ROMAN-STYLE PIZZAS, CUT TO order by the square and served at room temperature. Many of our staples I included in my first book, *My Bread*, and so I have devoted this chapter to our newer pizzas, and a stand-mixer version of pizza bianca. Any of these pizzas work well as appetizers—the larger pies work very well when cut into fifteen small squares and served with wine. Slightly larger slices accompanied by a salad make for an excellent dinner.

Pizza bianca (page 118).

PIZZA BIANCA ALLA ROMANA, VERSION 2

(This recipe can be "kneaded" with a stand mixer.)

This is a speedier version of pizza bianca than the one on page 65. Here, a stand-mixer and instant yeast provide a shortcut dough for pizza bianca or to use as a base for the pizzas that follow. This recipe makes enough dough for two round pizza biancas or two of the rectangular pizzas featured in this chapter. If you only want to make one pizza, freeze half the dough or cut the recipe in half.

YIELD: Two 12-inch round pizza biancas
EQUIPMENT: A pizza stone, a 12-inch-wide pizza peel, and two 12-by-16-inch pieces of parchment paper

Extra virgin olive oil for brushing on the bowl and pizzas

500 grams (3⅓ cups) unbleached all-purpose flour, plus flour for shaping

5 grams (1 heaping teaspoon) sugar

5 grams (scant 1 teaspoon) salt

2 grams (⅔ teaspoon) fast-acting/instant yeast (3 grams, or 1 teaspoon, in winter)

440 grams (scant 2 cups) room-temperature (65° to 70°F) water

6 grams (1½ teaspoons) coarse sea salt

A handful of fresh rosemary for serving (optional)

1. Lightly oil a very large mixing bowl and set aside. Fit a stand mixer with a pastry paddle/flat beater. Mix the flour, sugar, fine sea salt, and yeast in the mixer bowl on the slowest speed until they are just combined. Add the water, mix slowly for 30 more seconds, then turn to the highest speed and mix for 2½ to 4 minutes, until the dough comes together. You'll know when the dough is ready because it will suddenly come off the sides of the bowl and wrap itself around the pastry paddle and start to slap the bowl. It will look as though the dough is trying to climb the paddle. The texture will be stringy and elastic. Gently peel the dough from the paddle and scrape the dough into the oiled mixing bowl. Cover the bowl with a tea towel and let the dough proof at room temperature until it doubles in size and is wonderfully bubbly, 1½ to 2 hours.

2. Dust flour over two 12-by-16-inch pieces of parchment paper. Dust a little flour over the risen dough in the bowl. Lightly flour your hands. Using a dough scraper or a knife, divide the dough in half. Pinch off one half of the dough and, with gravity's help, form the dough into a

taut ball and place seam side down on one piece of the floured parchment. Dust a bit more flour on the paper, if needed, so that there is a coating of flour on the paper all around the dough. Repeat with the second half of the dough.

3. Use a pastry brush to coat the centers of the tops of each round of dough with olive oil. (Leave a margin of several inches around the perimeter; the oil will spread on its own.) Sprinkle the coarse sea salt on top of the oil. Let the dough rounds sit, uncovered, at room temperature, until they have doubled in size, 1 to 3 hours. When they are ready, the doughs will be large, bubbly, expansive, and clearly full of gas. Place a pizza stone on the middle rack of the oven and heat it to 500°F.

4. Dust the tops of the doughs lightly with flour and gently pull the dough outward with both hands so that it stretches to about 8 inches in diameter. I call this movement "opening the dough." Now for 10 seconds of fun: Stick out all ten of your fingers like you're going to try to walk across the table with them and "dock," or dimple, both doughs by plunging your fingers into them very firmly, three or four times for each dough.

> **Note on docking:** The perfect amount of docking, or dimpling the dough, will give pizza bianca a sublime texture—pliant, soft, and bubbly. Too much docking will create a hard disk. Here is how I recommend doing it: press all 10 of your fingers firmly into one of the doughs. Press quite hard—enough to feel the surface below and leave a firm impression in the dough—but not so hard that you rip a hole in the dough. Repeat three or four times and then do the same for the other dough. The impressions will turn into craters and valleys and give the finished surface the appearance of a lunar landscape.

5. Place one docked pizza dough on parchment onto the peel. Oil or flour your fingertips and dock the dough again, with both hands, about three times. Very gently, use your fingertips to pull the dough outward all around—it should stretch evenly to make a rough circle that nearly reaches the edges of the parchment and is about 12 inches in diameter.

6. Open the oven, line up the far end of the peel with the far end of the pizza stone, and slip the pizza on the parchment onto the stone. Bake for about 7 minutes.

(CONTINUES)

7. Open the oven and quickly slip the parchment out from beneath the pizza. Shut the oven and continue to bake for 6 to 7 minutes, until the top of the pizza is browning and the valleys made by your fingertips are pale and golden. Slide the peel under the pizza and transfer it to a wire rack to cool for 5 minutes. If you don't have a wire rack, lean the pizza on its side for a few minutes. This will allow the bottom to cool and prevent it from becoming soft.

8. Now that the peel is free, place the second pizza on parchment and repeat the docking and stretching. Bake the second pizza. Brush the warm pizzas generously with olive oil, sprinkle with rosemary needles (if using), and serve.

CAPICOLA

capicola pizza with fermented chile peppers

This is my idea of a perfect savory food: sweet, spicy, and salty. Capicola is a type of cured pork that is similar to prosciutto. It is lean and perfectly round, making it perfect for assembling an obsessively symmetrical pizza such as this.

YIELD: One 18-by-13-inch pizza
EQUIPMENT: One 18-by-13-inch rimmed baking sheet and a pizza stone (you can make this without a pizza stone underneath the sheet pan, but the crust will not be as crisp)

½ fennel bulb (150 grams), cored and very thinly sliced

15 grams (1 tablespoon) extra virgin olive oil, plus oil for the pan

Coarsely ground fresh black pepper

½ batch Pizza Bianca alla Romana, Version 2 (page 118) or Version 1 (page 65), made through step 3

227 grams (8 ounces) mascarpone

15 pitted Castelvetrano or other pitted green olives

⅔ cup Lacto-Fermented Chile Peppers (page 198) (sriracha is a fine substitute)

15 thin slices capicola

1. Place a pizza stone on middle rack in the oven and heat to 450°F.

2. Toss the fennel slices with the olive oil and black pepper to taste and set aside. Lightly oil an 18-by-13-inch rimmed sheet pan.

3. Place one ball of dough in the center of the oiled pan. Gently tug the dough so that it fits the pan. Take care not to deflate the dough.

4. Arrange 15 dollops of mascarpone across the dough in three rows of five. Place an olive in each mascarpone dollop. Distribute the chiles and then the fennel evenly across the pizza. Place a slice of capicola over each olive. Allow to proof at room temperature for 20 minutes, then bake for 25 to 30 minutes—placing the sheet pan directly on the baking stone—until the capicola is crisp and the crust is lightly browned.

(CONTINUES)

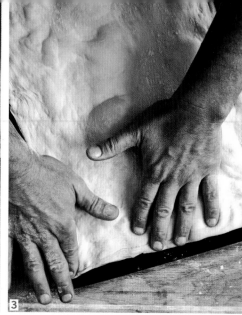

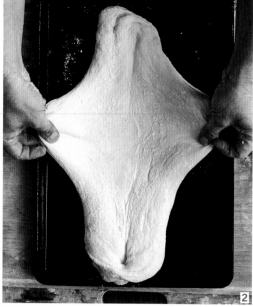

Capicola Pizza, in Pictures

1 Place the dough in the center of the pan and stretch lengthwise.

2 Gently tug the dough outward to the sides.

3 Pat the dough lightly but firmly to reach all the edges.

4 Space 15 dollops of mascarpone in three rows of five. Top each with an olive.

5 Drizzle on the chiles.

6 Scatter the fennel evenly.

7 Place a slice of capicola over each olive.

8 Wait 20 minutes for the dough to rise a bit before baking.

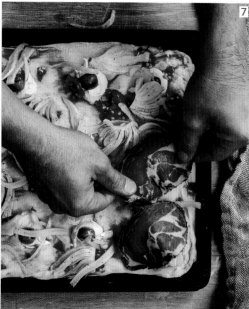

Capicola pizza just out of the oven.

MELE E FINOCCHIO

apple-fennel pizza

The fennel in this pizza is an all-star: it does double duty in the flavor department as it crisps on the top of the pizza and turns meltingly soft on the bottom layer. Eat this pizza once it has cooled off—the apple will be deliciously sweet, the fennel crisp, and both will be better off with the little bit of salty pancetta.

YIELD: One 18-by-13-inch pizza

EQUIPMENT: One 18-by-13-inch rimmed sheet pan and a pizza stone (you can make this without a pizza stone underneath the sheet pan, but the crust will not be as crisp)

½ large fennel bulb (115 grams), cored and thinly sliced (about 15 pieces)

15 grams (1 tablespoon) extra virgin olive oil

0.5 gram (⅛ teaspoon) freshly ground black pepper

½ batch Pizza Bianca alla Romana, Version 2 (page 118) or Version 1 (page 65), made through step 3

15 slices (200 grams) Brie

2 tart green apples (115 grams), cored and sliced (15 slices)

50 grams (2 heaping tablespoons) very finely chopped pancetta

2 rosemary sprigs (15 needles)

Fine sea salt to taste

1. Place a pizza stone on the middle rack of the oven and heat the oven to 450°F. Lightly oil an 18-by-13-inch rimmed sheet pan.

2. Toss the fennel slices in the olive oil and a pinch of black pepper and set aside.

3. Place one ball of dough in the center of the oiled sheet pan. Gently tug the dough so that it fits the pan. Take care not to deflate the dough. Arrange 15 slices of Brie evenly across the dough, in three rows of five. Scatter half the fennel over the dough, then layer one apple slice over each cheese slice. Next layer on the pancetta and remaining fennel and place one rosemary needle in the center of each apple. Let proof at room temperature for 20 minutes, season with salt, and bake for 25 minutes, placing the sheet pan on top of the baking stone. The pizza is done when the crust has puffed up and is lightly browned and the apples are slightly soft.

Apple-fennel pizza.

Carrot pizza with clementines and olives.

CAROTA

carrot pizza with clementines and olives

This pizza is inspired by a salad made by Jean-Georges Vongerichten at ABC Kitchen. The salad is composed of whole roasted carrots, cumin, and creamy cheese, and I found it the most compelling combination. I love how the sweetness of a perfectly cooked carrot and the richness of cream cheese melt together.

YIELD: One 18-by-13-inch pizza
EQUIPMENT: One 18-by-13-inch rimmed baking pan and a pizza stone (you can make this without a pizza stone underneath the sheet pan, but the crust will not be as crisp)

2 medium carrots (300 grams), peeled and shaved or very thinly sliced

½ teaspoon red pepper flakes

½ batch Pizza Bianca alla Romana, Version 2 (page 118) or Version 1 (page 65), made through step 3

8 grams (1½ teaspoons) extra virgin olive oil, plus oil for the pan and the pizza

6 ounces cream cheese, softened

2 clementines, unpeeled, halved lengthwise, thinly sliced, and seeded

15 pitted oil-cured black olives

1 teaspoon cumin seeds

¼ teaspoon coarse sea salt

½ cup chopped fresh cilantro

1. Place a pizza stone on the middle rack of the oven and heat to 450°F. Lightly oil an 18-by-13-inch rimmed baking sheet.

2. Toss the red pepper flakes and carrots in a bowl with the olive oil and set aside.

3. Place one ball of dough in the center of the oiled sheet pan. Gently tug the dough so that it fits the pan. Take care not to deflate the dough. Arrange 15 dollops of cream cheese across the dough in three rows of five. Scatter the clementine pieces and olives on top, followed by the carrots. Drizzle olive oil over the pizza, then scatter on the cumin seeds. Sprinkle with salt to taste. Allow to proof at room temperature for 20 minutes, then bake for 25 minutes, placing the sheet pan directly onto the baking stone. When the pizza is done, remove from the oven and scatter the cilantro leaves across the pizza.

Asparagus pizza.

ASPARAGUS PIZZA

This pizza is topped with handfuls of asparagus shredded with a vegetable peeler. The peeling takes a bit of time, but the texture of the roasted ribbons is crispy vegetable heaven and totally worth the trouble.

YIELD: One 18-by-13-inch pizza
EQUIPMENT: One 18-by-13-inch rimmed baking sheet and a pizza stone (you can make this without a pizza stone underneath the sheet pan, but the crust will not be as crisp)

Olive oil for the pan and the pizza
½ batch Pizza Bianca alla Romana, Version 2 (page 118) or Version 1 (page 65), made through step 3
200 grams (1 cup) Brie
1 large garlic clove

25 grams (about 1 ounce) grated Parmigiano-Reggiano cheese
Freshly ground black pepper
454 grams (1 pound) asparagus, shaved
3 grams (½ teaspoon) coarse sea salt
Grated zest of ½ Meyer or other lemon

1. Place a pizza stone on the middle rack of the oven and heat oven to 500°F. Lightly oil a sheet pan.

2. Place one ball of dough in the center of the oiled sheet pan. Gently tug the dough so that it fits the pan. Take care not to deflate the dough.

3. Arrange 15 pieces (about 1 tablespoon each) of Brie across the dough in three rows of five. Using a box grater, grate the garlic clove over the top, then scatter on the Parmigiano-Reggiano and black pepper. Add the shaved asparagus in big handfuls across the pizza. Top with sea salt and bake for 18 minutes, placing the sheet pan directly onto the pizza stone. The asparagus will char in places, which is good! Drizzle on olive oil and sprinkle the lemon zest over the top of the pizza and serve.

* eating

If you like beer, serve this with a crisp wheat hefeweizen.

Cardamom cinnamon buns (page 147).

6

BREAKFAST
AT THE BAKERY

BAKERIES TEND TO BE SYNONYMOUS WITH EARLY MORNING HOURS. WE ARE open early, but we're also a New York City bakery, and we've found that people come in all day long looking for breakfast. (Whether this is because they've just woken up or because they equate bakeries with breakfast I'm not sure.) At our café we serve bowls of soft-cooked eggs and toast, as well as small, muffiny cakes throughout the day. I've learned a few things from doing this. The first is that New Yorkers love eggs at all hours of the day. The second is that there is no wrong time to have a *tortino*—the little cakes we set out for breakfast. For breakfast, for a little treat with a cup of coffee, or for dessert—they get eaten every which way.

I squirrel them away sometimes as treats for my kids, I eat them in the middle of the night when I'm looking for snacks, and if there are any left, I eat them first thing in the morning for breakfast. They are just as versatile when baking them at home: the Olanda (page 145) and the Orange Olive-Oil Cake (page 142) keep so well that they can even be made a day or two ahead of when you're planning to serve them.

UOVO IN COPPETTA
poached eggs and toast

Phyllis O'Hara, my grandmother, was an Irish Catholic from Liverpool, England. Unlike me, she was very proper. When I went to her house, she would make me the most perfect meal: lightly poached eggs and slices of buttered toast. When I was a child, I had no idea that eggs and soldiers, as it's sometimes known, had a name or that it was British. I just knew it as a perfect thing to eat. I still think the combination is both correct and sublime. It's one of my favorite things to eat, and we serve it all day at the café (although now I add vegetables!).

My grandmother taught me to poach eggs in the shell. The finished eggs are very delicate and oozy. If you prefer a firmer sort of egg, you might fry the eggs sunny side up or over easy for any of the egg recipes that follow.

YIELD: Serves 2   PLAN AHEAD: Warm 2 small serving bowls in the oven at 200°F.

4 large eggs	**4 slices of bread, toasted, buttered, and cut in 1- to 2-inch cubes**

1. Fill a 3-quart pot three-quarters full of water and bring to a boil. Place the eggs in a bowl near the cooktop.

2. Turn down the heat on the water to keep it at a rolling boil. Use a large slotted spoon to gently lower the eggs into the water one by one in quick succession. If your eggs have been refrigerated, cook uncovered at a simmer for exactly 5 minutes. If your eggs have been stored at room temperature, cook them uncovered at a simmer for exactly 4 minutes. Halfway through cooking, give the eggs a tap with a heavy spoon to crack the shell. This will make for easier peeling later. If a little of the white comes out, that's okay. Divide the toast between two small serving bowls and keep them warm.

3. When the eggs are done, use a slotted spoon to gently lift the eggs out of the saucepan. Place the eggs on a plate and allow to cool and continue cooking for 1 minute.

4. Peel the eggs. They should come out quite easily, but you may want to do this over or very near the bowls of buttered toast, just in case. Set two eggs on top of the buttered toast in each bowl. Give the eggs another nice whack with a spoon to shatter them. The yolks should ooze out dramatically.

(CONTINUES)

> **Note:** If you are cooking several batches of eggs and you leave the water boiling in between batches, you may need to top the water off to make sure that there is always enough water to cover the eggs.

UOVO IN COPPETTA AL ITALIANA

eggs in a bowl with arugula and tomatoes

Truccio Saré, Whole Wheat Sourdough (page 93), is my favorite bread to serve in this dish. I like to assemble all of the ingredients and have them ready to receive the eggs as soon as they are cooked.

YIELD: Serves 2 PLAN AHEAD: Warm 2 small serving bowls in the oven at 200°F.

1 cup arugula

4 Oven-Dried Tomatoes (page 201) or 4 slices fresh tomato, lightly salted

4 slices whole wheat bread, toasted, buttered, and cut in cubes

4 large eggs, poached and peeled (page 133)

5 grams (1 teaspoon) extra virgin olive oil or to taste

Coarse sea salt

Freshly ground black pepper

A few shavings of Parmigiano-Reggiano cheese

½ teaspoon finely chopped fresh oregano

Layer the arugula, tomatoes, and buttered toast in the serving bowls. Top the toast with the eggs, a drizzle of olive oil, salt and pepper to taste, and a bit of shaved Parmigiano-Reggiano. Sprinkle on the oregano.

farmer style

You can precook the vegetables the day or night before (or use up leftovers if you have them): just heat them in the oven before you start the eggs; you'll need a few extra minutes to heat them or, in the case of potatoes and onions, brown them a bit. I like to cook bacon just until the fat has turned an amber color—like a golden India Pale Ale beer.

(CONTINUES)

Uovo in coppetta al Italiana, farmer style.

Fine sea salt

4 strips bacon

1 medium Idaho potato, peeled and cut into 4 wedges

1 medium spring onion or scallion, white and green parts, quartered with root still attached (this will keep the onion from separating in the water)

4 large eggs

¼ cup chopped fresh parsley or basil

5 grams (1 teaspoon) extra virgin olive oil or to taste

Freshly ground black pepper

1. Heat the oven to 400°F. Fill a 3-quart saucepan three-quarters full of water and bring to a boil over high heat. Add a generous teaspoon of salt to the water. Cook the bacon on a sheet pan for 11 to 13 minutes or until the fat is amber. When the bacon is done, drain on paper towels, then slice into 1-inch squares and set aside. Pour the bacon fat from the pan. Save the pan for browning the potatoes and onions. Increase the oven temperature to 450°F.

2. Reduce the water to medium-low and simmer the potatoes in the salted water for 10 minutes or until tender. Remove the potatoes with a slotted spoon and place on paper towels to dry. Drop the onion into the water and simmer for 2 minutes. Remove the onion with a slotted spoon and drain with the potatoes. Allow both to dry. Transfer to the reserved sheet pan and bake for 7 minutes or until they begin to brown.

3. Add more water to the saucepan, if needed, and return the water to a simmer. Poach and peel the eggs as directed on page 133.

4. Divide the potatoes and onion between the warm serving bowls and top with the eggs, bacon, and herbs. Drizzle with olive oil and season with salt and pepper to taste.

CON CAVALO E CIPOLLA
with kale and caramelized onions

This dish features lacinato kale and onions that have been browned and caramelized—what an Italian would call *rosolare*. Lacinato kale is also known as Tuscan, black, or dinosaur kale. It is a very dark green, with bumpy leaves.

15 grams (1 tablespoon) plus 5 grams (1 teaspoon) extra virgin olive oil

1 medium onion, halved lengthwise and thinly sliced

⅛ teaspoon fine sea salt

8 lacinato kale leaves, stemmed and roughly chopped

4 slices bread, toasted, buttered, and cubed

4 large eggs, poached and pulled (page 133)

1 tablespoon soft, shavable cheese such as young pecorino Toscano, mild cheddar, or Havarti

5 grams (1 teaspoon) extra virgin olive oil or to taste

Coarse salt

Freshly ground black pepper

1. Heat a medium skillet over medium heat until it is just hot. Add 1 tablespoon of the olive oil, the onion, and a healthy pinch of fine sea salt. Give the onion a stir or two to coat it with oil and then lower the heat. Cover and let the onion steam for about 5 minutes, until translucent, giving the pan a shake halfway through. Uncover the saucepan, raise the heat, and continue to cook, stirring occasionally to prevent sticking, for 3 to 4 minutes or until the onion begins to caramelize. Add the kale and cook for 2 more minutes.

2. Divide the toast between the warm serving bowls and top with the onion and kale. Top with the eggs and shave a few ribbons of cheese over the eggs. Drizzle with olive oil and season with coarse salt and pepper to taste.

AL MEXICANO

with kale pico de gallo

If you have some Lacto-Fermented Chile Peppers (page 198), serve a spoonful in each bowl.

2 ripe plum tomatoes, seeded and chopped

1 jalapeño chile, seeded and finely chopped

2 scallions, white and green parts, finely chopped

2 tablespoons chopped fresh cilantro

4 kale leaves, sliced into thin ribbons

4 slices of bread, toasted, buttered, and cubed

4 large eggs, poached and peeled (page 133)

5 grams (1 teaspoon) extra virgin olive oil or to taste

Fine sea salt

Freshly ground black pepper

1. Combine the tomatoes, jalapeño, scallions, cilantro, and kale in a small bowl.

2. Divide the toast between the warm bowls and top with the eggs and the kale pico de gallo. Drizzle with olive oil and season with salt and pepper to taste.

PANINI D'UOVO

egg sandwiches

Like many New Yorkers, I love a corner-deli egg sandwich in the morning. When I opened the bakery café in Chelsea, one of the first things I wanted to do was make an awesome Italianish egg sandwich. We ended up serving them all day because they are so popular—and we had to come up with a way to have perfectly soft scrambled eggs ready at all times. We settled on soft-boiling eggs, roughly chopping them, and blitzing them with olive oil. When we toast them in a hot oven, they emerge virtually indistinguishable from a fluffy scrambled egg. This perfect practical solution came from our manager at the time, George Kantlis. He had been using this method at home as a way to replicate one of his own treasured childhood food memories—eating his Greek mother's perfectly soft-cooked eggs, on fresh bread, with salt and a hearty drizzle of olive oil. At the bakery we serve our egg sandwiches on brioche rolls (page 111), but they are also nice on ciabatta (page 85).

YIELD: Serves 4   EQUIPMENT: A food processor

FAUX-SCRAMBLED EGGS:

7 large eggs, cold from the refrigerator
60 grams (¼ cup) extra virgin olive oil

½ teaspoon fine sea salt

1. Bring a medium pot of water to a boil. Use a spoon to carefully lower each egg into the water in quick succession. Maintain at a rolling boil; after exactly 6 minutes, pull the eggs from the water and transfer to a bowl. Let stand at room temperature for 10 minutes (the carry-over heat will continue the cooking process), and then cool completely in the refrigerator.

2. Peel the eggs, place in a food processor, and pulse four or five times with the olive oil and salt. The eggs will resemble scrambled eggs. In this state the eggs will keep, refrigerated, for 1 day.

3. When ready to serve the eggs, spread 2 tablespoons of the egg mixture onto lightly buttered bread and bake at 500°F for 4 minutes or until the eggs are warmed through.

ORIGINALE

egg sandwich with crispy prosciutto

8 thin slices prosciutto

10 grams (2 teaspoons) salted butter

4 wedges Pizza Bianca (page 65 or 118) split open lengthwise like clamshells, or 4 slices of bread

1 batch Faux-Scrambled Eggs (page 138)

8 fresh basil leaves

4 Oven-Dried Tomatoes (page 201), cut into thirds, or 4 slices very ripe fresh tomatoes, lightly salted

1. Heat the oven to 400°F. Place the prosciutto on a parchment-paper-lined sheet pan and bake for 14 minutes or until crispy. Set aside and turn the oven up to 500°F or the highest temperature of your oven.

2. Lightly butter the bread. Fill the bread slices with 2 tablespoons of the eggs and bake for 4 minutes. Top the eggs with the basil, tomatoes, and prosciutto. Close up the sandwiches and serve immediately.

VARIATIONS

SALCICCIA

with sausage, provolone, and fried sage

Fry 12 fresh sage leaves in 2 tablespoons butter until crispy; set aside. Butter the bread and spread the eggs on the bottom slices. Top with 50 grams (2 heaping tablespoons) crumbled cooked sausage. Lay one slice of provolone on each top slice. Bake as directed. Lay the fried sage leaves on the sausage and egg and complete the sandwiches.

FORMAGGIO

with cheese

Butter the bread, put the eggs on the bottom slices, and top the egg with 20 grams (1 tablespoon) shredded Gouda or aged cheddar. Bake as directed, until the cheese is bubbling. Drizzle the egg with a few drops of lemon juice and olive oil and a few shavings of Parmigiano-Reggiano. Top with freshly cracked black pepper.

TORTINO DI CRUSCA

bran and blackberry muffins

As an Italian-inspired baker, I spend an unusual amount of time thinking about wheat bran. It started in Genzano, a small town outside Rome in the Frascati hills. It's known for its ancient villas and vineyards, but my time there was spent in clouds of bran. The bakers there used it for everything—in bread, on bread, under bread; it was thrown by the handful onto every visible work surface to keep the doughs from sticking. At the end of the day even the floors were covered in bran. The bakers would sweep it into piles, pick out the cigarette butts (this was Rome in the early 1990s), and save it for the next day. I fell in love with the toasty flavor of the bran, and I adopted many of these uses (excluding, of course, the smoking and the sweepings). It's a great way to keep dough from sticking to things, it's tidier than flour, and it seems natural to bake bread using the bran of the wheat as both a tool and an ingredient.

I love the way bran tastes in breads and on bread and the way it perfumes the bakery while it toasts. Eventually it occurred to me that I could honor the bran by making something special with it, and we started making these little cakes, or tortini. I like to add blackberries because I enjoy their size and flavor. If you decide to use another berry instead, be careful—some particularly juicy berries, such as those larger, cultivated blueberries—end up being too wet to work well here.

YIELD: 12 muffins   EQUIPMENT: A muffin pan and paper liners

165 grams (1 cup plus 2 tablespoons) unbleached all-purpose flour

5 grams (1 teaspoon) baking soda

55 grams (¾ cup) wheat bran

2 grams (½ teaspoon) fine sea salt

113 grams (1 stick/8 tablespoons) unsalted butter at room temperature

78 grams (⅓ cup) packed light brown sugar

1 large egg

2 grams (1 teaspoon) vanilla extract

95 grams (4½ tablespoons) honey

220 grams (scant 1 cup) Greek-style yogurt at room temperature

340 grams (12 ounces) blackberries

30 grams (⅓ cup) rolled oats

1. Heat the oven to 425°F and line a 12-cup muffin tin with papers. Whisk the flour, baking soda, wheat bran, and salt into a medium bowl.

2. With an electric mixer, cream the butter and brown sugar together at medium speed in a large bowl until they are light and fluffy. Add the egg and continue mixing until well combined; then add the vanilla and honey.

3. Use a rubber spatula to gently fold in half of the dry ingredients. Stop folding while you can still see streaks of flour. Add half of the yogurt and stir; stop while streaks of yogurt are still visible. Fold in the remainder of the dry ingredients, followed by the remainder of the yogurt, in the same fashion. Take care to scrape the bottom and sides of the bowl to incorporate any clumps of flour or yogurt. Mix until almost combined and then gently fold in half of the blackberries.

4. Scoop the batter into the cups in the muffin tin, filling each about three-quarters full. Press the remaining half of the blackberries into the tops of the muffins. Scatter the rolled oats on top of the muffins and bake for 20 to 25 minutes or until the muffin tops turn a deep golden hue, develop a slight crust, and spring back to the touch. Transfer the muffins to a wire rack to cool.

TORTA D'OLIO D'OLIVA

orange olive-oil cake

> **Note:** Use a high-quality fruity extra virgin olive oil, since the cake will take on its flavors. And if you have coarse sea salt, use that—it doesn't dissolve all the way in the cake, and the little pockets of saltiness bring out the sweetness in the other bites.

This recipe is one of my favorites. It is easy to make, it's extremely versatile, and the enormous amount of olive oil makes for a luscious texture and beautiful color. And, of course, a cake made with olive oil elicits no guilt and is perfect at all times of the day. It's good for breakfast with hot coffee and fresh fruit. It's good for lunch. It's nice with ice cream. It's marvelous with prosecco. I like it best in winter, when its golden color and bits of citrus brighten our cold northeastern mornings.

YIELD: One 8-inch round cake   EQUIPMENT: An 8-inch round metal cake pan

200 grams (1¼ cups plus 2 tablespoons) unbleached all-purpose flour	Grated or chopped zest of 2 large navel oranges
5 grams (1 teaspoon) baking powder	2 large eggs
2.5 grams (½ teaspoon) baking soda	63 grams (¼ cup) fresh orange juice
4 grams (¾ teaspoon) coarse sea salt	158 grams (⅔ cup) whole milk
200 grams (1 cup) sugar	153 grams (¾ cup) extra virgin olive oil

1. Heat the oven to 350°F. Place a rack in the bottom third of the oven. Line the bottom of an 8-inch cake pan with a circle of parchment paper. Whisk the flour, baking powder, baking soda, and salt in a large bowl to combine. Whisk the sugar, zest, eggs, orange juice, milk, and olive oil in a medium bowl until well combined.

2. Make a well in the dry ingredients and pour in the wet ingredients. Use a rubber spatula to mix together quickly and evenly until just combined. Take care to scrape the sides and bottom of the bowl to be sure you don't miss any clumps. Pour the batter into the cake pan and bake until the center of the cake springs back and there is a beautiful, even, nut brown crust—about 50 minutes. Allow the cake to cool on a rack in the pan for a few minutes. Run a knife around the edge and then turn it out onto a plate.

> **Make It Ahead:** All the olive oil in this cake means you needn't bother to oil the pan. The olive oil also keeps the cake moist and flavorful for several days. You can safely bake this a day or two in advance of when you need it and serve it at room temperature.

Orange olive-oil cake.

Banana chocolate-chip cake.

OLANDA

banana chocolate-chip cake

Bananas seem like such an ordinary ingredient today, but there was a point in time when bananas—as well as chocolate and coffee—were exotic items for those of us in the northern hemisphere. I've always liked combining these imported staples; it makes me think of spice merchants traveling the globe, finding expensive and unusual flavors in faraway lands. Holland—*Olanda* in Italian—was one of the first great global trading empires, and in my mind, these fruits and spices all have a home on a seventeenth-century Dutch trading ship. (I also adore the undulating oceanic beauty of the name Olanda.)

YIELD: One 8-inch round cake   EQUIPMENT: An 8-inch round metal cake pan

80 grams (1½ sticks/12 tablespoons) unsalted butter

160 grams (1 cup plus 1 tablespoon and 1 teaspoon) unbleached all-purpose flour

6 grams (1¼ teaspoons) baking powder

1 gram (¼ teaspoon) fine sea salt

40 grams (¼ cup) extra virgin olive oil

80 grams (scant ½ cup) granulated sugar

40 grams (¼ cup) packed dark brown sugar

20 grams (1 tablespoon) molasses

1 gram (½ teaspoon) ground allspice

1 gram (½ teaspoon) ground cinnamon

7 grams (1½ teaspoons) espresso or strong coffee, cooled

2 grams (½ teaspoon) vanilla extract

1 large egg

200 grams (1 cup) chunky, well-smashed ripe bananas (about 2 medium)

120 grams (½ cup plus 1 tablespoon) semisweet chocolate chips

1. Using a bit of the butter, grease an 8-inch round metal cake pan and line the bottom with a circle of parchment paper. Heat the oven to 425°F.

2. Whisk together the flour, baking powder, and salt in a small bowl. In a large bowl with an electric mixer on low speed, beat the butter, olive oil, white and brown sugars, molasses, spices, coffee, and vanilla until well combined. The secret to this cake is to stop creaming *before* the sugar is dissolved.

3. Crack the egg into the sugar and butter mixture and beat with a spoon so that the mixture becomes light and fluffy.

(CONTINUES)

4. Add the dry ingredients to the batter and mix with a flexible spatula until there are still streaks of flour in the mix. Gently fold in the chocolate chips and bananas and stop as soon as everything is combined. Pour the mixture into the prepared pan. Bake for about 25 minutes, until the top is a deep golden brown, the center springs back to the touch, and the sides just begin to pull away from the sides of the pan. Once it's cooled a bit, run a knife along the edge and turn out onto a plate.

5. Serve warm or store tightly covered for a day.

SPIRALI DI CANNELLA

cardamom cinnamon buns

(This recipe requires the brioche dough on page 107.)

The smell of cardamom is intoxicating. Floral, fruity, and imbued with a cool sweetness, cardamom marries well with the warm bite of cinnamon and a citrus glaze.

To have these rolls bright and early in the morning, make the brioche and allow it to fully ferment. Place the dough in the refrigerator overnight. In the morning, assemble the rolls and allow them to proof until doubled and then bake and drizzle with the citrus icing.

YIELD: 12 cinnamon rolls   EQUIPMENT: A 13-by-9-by-2-inch baking pan
PLAN AHEAD: Have the brioche dough made through step 3

118 grams (½ cup) packed dark brown sugar

3 grams (1 teaspoon) ground cinnamon

2 grams (½ teaspoon) ground green cardamom

1 batch fully fermented No-Knead, Naturally Leavened Brioche (page 107) dough

5 grams (1 teaspoon) water

80 grams (¾ cup) chopped pecans (optional)

30 grams (2 tablespoons) fresh orange or lemon juice

100 grams (scant 1 cup) confectioners' sugar, sifted

1. Line a 13-by-9-by-2-inch baking pan with parchment paper. Mix the brown sugar, cinnamon, and cardamom together in a small bowl.

2. Working on a floured work surface, use a floured rolling pin to gently roll the dough out into a rough rectangle ¼ inch thick, 12 inches wide, and 18 inches long. Mix the water into the cinnamon sugar and spread the mixture over the dough. Sprinkle with the pecans if using, right up to the edges. Shape the dough into a log by rolling the long side of the rectangle gently toward you. Roll firmly but gently until it is a neat cylinder. With a ruler as your guide, use a sharp knife to make small marks in the dough at 1½-inch intervals. Quickly slice through the markings and place the rolls ½ inch apart on the parchment-lined baking pan. Loosely cover with a damp tea towel and set aside to proof until they are doubled in size, about 2 to 3 hours.

(CONTINUES)

3. Heat the oven to 400°F. Uncover the buns. Bake until the buns begin to brown lightly on top, about 18 minutes. Remove the rolls from the oven. Make a glaze by whisking the citrus juice with the confectioners' sugar. Drizzle over the swirls and eat immediately.

> **Note:** If you are baking in a warm climate and having difficulty with the stickiness of the brioche dough, you can refrigerate the dough for ½ hour before you work with it. The butter in the dough will stiffen and make the dough firmer and easier to work with.

Cardamom cinnamon buns (page 146).

CHOCOLATE SWIRL BRIOCHE LOAF

(This recipe requires the brioche dough on page 107.)

Today I am considered a wee bit eccentric, but in my early twenties I was a loose cannon. At the time, I was enrolled at the School of Visual Arts, in Manhattan, and part of my ritual was to stop on the way home at Moishe's, a bakery in the East Village. Moishe's was always bustling with bemused customers, impatient clerks, and a ceaseless cascade of Yiddish complaints. I felt absolutely at home. On every visit I would buy a chocolate babka—a sweet yeasted bread with a chocolate filling. These chocolate babkas were big and buttery and contained a fantastic amount of dark chocolate. My pilgrimages to Moishe's ended when I was kicked out of art school for being disruptive—but now every time I make a brioche loaf, I think of Moishe's babkas, and there are times I am unable to restrain myself from adding in a devious vein of rich chocolate.

YIELD: One 8½-by-4½-inch loaf   EQUIPMENT: A food processor and an 8½-by-4½-inch loaf pan

120 grams (¾ cup) bittersweet chocolate cut into pieces

15 grams (1 tablespoon) brown sugar

6 grams (1 tablespoon) dark cocoa powder

15 grams (1 tablespoon) water

70 grams (2½ tablespoons) cream cheese

1 batch No-Knead, Naturally Leavened Brioche (page 107) dough, made through step 3

Unbleached all-purpose flour for the work surface

1. Line an 8½-by-4½-inch loaf pan with parchment paper, leaving 2 inches of paper hanging over the ends. Place the chocolate pieces, brown sugar, and cocoa powder in a food processor. Pulse until combined (a smattering of chocolate lumps is okay). Set aside. In a small saucepan, warm the water and cream cheese, whisking to combine. Remove from the heat.

2. Place the fully leavened brioche dough on a lightly floured surface. Pat the dough down into a rectangle 7 by 14 inches. Spread the warm cream cheese on the dough, all the way to the edges. Sprinkle the chocolate mix on top. Roll the dough, nudging with a dough scraper if necessary, to form a 7-inch-long cylinder. Put the dough seam side down in the paper-lined loaf pan. Cover with a damp tea towel and let the loaf rise at room temperature until it reaches the top of the pan—2 to 4 hours in the summer and as many as 8 to 10 hours in the winter.

3. Heat the oven to 375°F. Remove the tea towel and bake the loaf, uncovered, for 45 to 50 minutes, until the top is light brown. (If the top begins to brown too quickly, cover it with foil, shiny side down.) Let the loaf cool for 5 minutes and then use the parchment paper to pull the loaf from the pan. Allow to cool on a wire rack before slicing.

Chocolate swirl brioche loaf.

Bomboloni with raspberry jelly.

BOMBOLONI
Italian doughnuts
(This recipe requires the brioche dough on page 107.)

It was a hot night in Rome the first time I had a bombolone. I was in my early twenties and had been out late with friends, and one of them "in the know" wanted to let me in on a late-night secret. He led me down a dark alley. I hardly knew what to expect—an ambush? But the only activity we found was an entrepreneuring baker selling midnight bomboloni out the back door of a bakery. The bomboloni were hot out of the fryer, and the cream inside was cool and freshly made. As we stood in the quiet alley eating these warm, sweet handfuls, I was giddy with delight.

Now, as then, I think that a freshly made bombolone—still hot from the fryer, snowy with powdered sugar, and plump with vanilla cream—is joy itself.

The dough and the pastry cream can be made a day ahead and refrigerated.

YIELD: 18 bomboloni
EQUIPMENT: A thermometer or deep fryer, a pastry bag or parchment cone, and a spider or skimmer
PLAN AHEAD: Make Vanilla Pastry Cream (page 156).

1 recipe No-Knead, Naturally Leavened Brioche (page 107) dough, made through step 3

Unbleached all-purpose flour for the work surface and pan

1 batch (about 3 cups) Vanilla Pastry Cream (page 156) or 360 grams (3 cups) jelly

Canola oil for frying (about 2 quarts)

50 grams (½ cup) confectioners' sugar

1. When the brioche dough has risen, turn it out onto a well-floured work surface and divide the dough with a dough scraper or knife into 18 equal parts weighing about 40 grams each. Shape the 18 pieces into balls by tugging the sides down, under, and into themselves to create a round shape with good surface tension (take care not to tear the dough, though). Let the balls rest 4 inches apart on a lightly floured sheet pan. Cover with a damp tea towel until they double in size, about 2 to 3 hours.

2. Fill a 3-quart saucepan two-thirds full with frying oil. Heat the oil to 350°F. Line a sheet pan with paper towels, place a wire rack on top, and put it near the frying area.

(CONTINUES)

> **The fry line:** The finished color of a well-cooked bombolone should be a light shade of hazelnut. When bomboloni are perfectly leavened, they will be light and fluffy and full of air, and bounce to the surface of the hot oil, leaving a pale "fry line," or ring, around their middle.

3. Gently lower the bomboloni into the hot oil using a slotted spoon, spider, or fry basket. As you lower them in, hold them suspended half out of the oil, for about 10 seconds, so that they puff up a bit. When you release them, they should bob and float to the surface. Flip them after 1 minute (I like to use a chopstick), and fry for 1½ minutes. Transfer to the wire rack to cool.

4. The doughnuts will continue to cook as they cool, so allow at least 10 minutes before filling or eating. Puncture the tops or sides with an implement the width of a chopstick or pencil. To fill the doughnuts, use a pastry bag or rolled-up parchment cone filled with the pastry cream or your favorite jelly (I like raspberry). Give each bombolone about 1½ tablespoons of filling. Dust with confectioners' sugar and serve immediately.

Bomboloni, in Pictures

1 When ready to fry, bomboloni will have nearly doubled in size.

2 A fry basket is the easiest way to keep track of your doughnuts.

3 Hold the doughnuts at the surface of the oil for about 10 seconds, to inflate.

4 If fully proofed, they will float. After a minute, gently turn them over.

5 Take note of the color—if the oil is too hot, they will turn a dark mahogany on the outside, while remaining raw on the inside.

6 After another 1½ minutes, remove from the oil. Repeat with the remaining doughnuts.

7 Let cool on a wire rack set on a sheet pan.

8 Wait at least 10 minutes before filling and sugaring.

CREMA PASTICCERA

vanilla pastry cream

I like using the seeds of a vanilla bean in my pastry cream. The fragrance is heady, and the flecks of vanilla are quite pretty. Use this pastry cream for bomboloni (page 153), pinolata (page 220), or focaccia fiorentina (page 223). This cream will keep refrigerated for up to 3 days.

YIELD: About 3 cups

36 grams (4 tablespoons) unbleached all-purpose flour

87 grams (6 tablespoons) sugar

1 large egg

1 egg yolk

500 grams (2 cups plus 1 tablespoon) whole milk

¼ vanilla bean, split and seeded

15 grams (1 tablespoon) unsalted butter

Combine the flour and sugar in a medium bowl. Whisk in the egg and egg yolk. Whisk in the milk until well incorporated. Pour the mixture into a medium saucepan. Add the vanilla bean and seeds. Bring the mixture to a boil over low heat, stirring constantly with a flexible spatula or flat-bottomed wooden spoon. Scrape the sides and bottom of the saucepan to prevent sticking. When the mixture has bubbled for 1 minute, remove from the heat. Strain the pastry cream into a bowl. Set the bowl into a larger bowl of ice. Rub the butter over the surface of the pastry cream to prevent a skin from forming.

CORNETTI

no-knead sourdough croissants
(This recipe requires the stiff starter, or biga, on page 51.)

Cornetti are to Italy what croissants are to France. They are not, however, the same thing. Cornetti are sweeter and cakier and are often filled with jam or cream. Nearly all widely distributed cornetti are factory made. This gives them a bit of a surreal aroma; to me, they smell like a candy shop version of a croissant. They are redolent of artificial vanilla and the soaring bouquets of other distinctly nonnatural additives. I didn't want to re-create these flavors exactly—but I liked to imagine what an "archetypal cornetto" would have tasted like had there been one. Here is my version of a sweet, flavorful, all-natural cornetto that is, of course, handmade and no-knead. At Sullivan Street Bakery, we make these by hand, every day, using this cousin of a brioche dough.

Much like croissants, cornetti take time to make, for they are fashioned by laminating the dough. This is a process of encapsulating a block of butter in the dough and completing a series of folds, rests, and rolls to produce layers upon layers of flaky dough and butter.

YIELD: 8 or 9 cornetti
EQUIPMENT: An 18-by-13-inch piece of parchment paper and a pizza cutter or sharp knife

250 grams (1¾ cups) unbleached all-purpose flour, plus flour for dusting

5 grams (scant 1 teaspoon) fine sea salt

2 grams (⅔ teaspoon) fast-acting/instant yeast

50 grams (¼ cup) whole milk

50 grams (¼ cup) water

153 grams (1⅓ sticks) cold unsalted butter

50 grams (¼ cup) sugar

1 large egg

20 grams biga (page 51)

1. Whisk the flour, salt, and yeast together in a medium bowl. Put the milk, water, and 3 grams of the butter into a saucepan and bring to a boil over medium heat. As soon as the mixture reaches a boil, add the sugar. Stir to dissolve the sugar, transfer the mixture to a large bowl, and allow to cool until tepid.

2. Whisk the egg and biga into the cooled liquids. Pour the contents of the flour bowl into the liquids and stir quickly to incorporate. The dough will be stiff.

(CONTINUES)

3. Allow the dough to sit, covered loosely, at room temperature for 2 hours. Pick the dough up, form into a ball, and flatten slightly. Wrap the dough tightly in plastic wrap and refrigerate for at least 4 hours (and as long as 8 to 10 hours).

4. Place the 150 grams of butter on a piece of parchment, and whack it with a rolling pin to soften the butter until it is just malleable and plastic, about the same texture as the dough. Form the butter into a block—about 1 inch tall and 3 inches square. Fold an 18-by-13-inch piece of parchment paper in three lengthwise. Place the butter square in the middle. Fold the two outer rectangles in so that the butter is enclosed, then fold in the bottom and top edges to make a perfect 5-inch square. Using a rolling pin, roll the butter out so that if fills the parchment square.

5. Have a small bowl of water handy. Remove the dough from the refrigerator and unwrap. On a very lightly floured work surface, roll the dough into a 12-inch circle about ¼ to ½ inch thick. Unwrap the butter block and place it in the middle of the dough so that it looks like diamond. Dip your finger in the water and moisten the edge of the dough circle.

6. Fold the upper left corner to the center of the butter square. Next, fold the upper right corner to the center of the butter square, allowing the dough to overlap slightly, pressing to seal. Continue clockwise around, making four folds total. Dip your fingers in the water and wet the edges of the dough to help the dough stick to itself. Press each seam firmly to seal. Turn the dough over so the seam side is down and allow to rest for 10 minutes. Roll the dough into a 12-inch square.

7. First fold: Fold the right side in about one-third, and then the left side over the top to align with the right edge, as you would a business letter. Wrap in plastic wrap and let rest in the refrigerator on a baking sheet for at least 1 hour and up to 3 hours.

8. Second fold: Remove from the refrigerator and let the dough come completely to room temperature, about 30 minutes. Place the dough on the lightly floured surface with the folded edges to the left and right and the open ends at the top and bottom. Roll out again until the dough measures roughly 18 inches from top to bottom and 8 inches from side to side. Fold the dough in thirds from top to bottom. Wrap the folded dough in plastic and let rest in the refrigerator for at least 1 hour and up to 3 hours.

9. Final roll: Remove from the refrigerator and let come to room temperature again. On a very lightly floured surface, place the dough as before with the folded edges on the right and left and the open ends at top and bottom. Roll the dough out again to make a rectangle that is approximately 16 inches from top to bottom and 8 inches from side to side.

10. Line a sheet pan with parchment. Use a sharp knife to trim a tiny bit off the sealed edges of the dough. (This will allow the layers to open as the cornetti bake.) Cut 8 triangles out of the dough. Each triangle should be 8 inches tall, with a base 3 inches across.

11. Cut a 1-inch slit in the base (shortest side) of each triangle. Pull the cut edges slightly apart and roll upward to the pointy end. Arrange the cornetti 4 inches apart on a parchment-lined baking sheet, cover with plastic wrap, and let proof for 12 hours or until the cornetti double in size. When lightly poked, an indentation will remain in the dough.

> **Note:** In very cold environments it can take as long as 24 hours for the cornetti to double in size.

12. Heat the oven to 400°F. Bake the cornetti for 14 to 16 minutes or until they are golden brown and the tops are crisp. Cool on a wire rack.

BUDINO DI MELE E PANE

apple bread pudding

I tried to come up with a good bread pudding recipe for twenty years. My stubbornness made the struggle difficult; I wanted to do it my own way, without looking at anyone else's recipe or asking for advice. It seemed like such a simple thing for a baker to do. Especially when surrounded by endless quantities of ever-staling bread. I finally discovered this combination one lucky day—when I looked around my kitchen and wondered what I was going to do with the piles of stale bread and the cold bag of apples I had brought home from the February farmers' market. For all the thought I gave bread pudding over the years, nothing worked half so well as this simple combination of two ingredients always on hand. They come together in the most sublime way, creating a heavenly combination of flavors that marries all the best things about apples, caramel, and French toast into one warm and soothing bite.

YIELD: One 9-inch round bread pudding; serves 6 to 8
EQUIPMENT: A 9-inch cake pan and a 12-inch square of foil

Oil for the foil

150 grams (¾ cup) sugar

500 grams (2 cups) half-and-half

5 large eggs

4 grams (1 teaspoon) vanilla extract

150 grams (4 cups) stale bread torn into 1½-inch pieces

2 large Braeburn apples, peeled, cored, and cut into 1½-inch pieces

15 grams (1 tablespoon) unsalted butter, softened

1. Place rack in the middle of the oven. Spray or lightly brush one side of a 12-inch square of foil with oil and set aside. Heat the oven to 450°F. Place the sugar in the bottom of a 9-inch round cake pan and shake it gently so the sugar is in an even layer. Bake the sugar for 12 to 14 minutes. The sugar will fully melt and turn a light amber color. Remove from the oven and let cool. The caramel will harden and may crack, making loud, startling pops. Lower the oven temperature to 400°F.

2. Whisk the half-and-half with the eggs and vanilla in a large bowl. Add the bread and apples and combine, using your hands or a spoon to mix until well combined.

3. Rub the surface of the cooled caramel and the sides of the pan with the butter. Pour the pudding mixture into the pan. Cover the pan with the foil. Place the pan on a rimmed baking sheet to catch any drips of caramel. Bake the pudding for 1 hour and 15 minutes or until puffy and set. Remove the pudding from the oven and remove the foil. Let the pudding cool for 2 minutes. Very carefully invert the pudding onto a serving plate. Let the pudding cool for at least 10 minutes before serving.

Braised brisket (page 188).

7

SLOW-COOKING
AND ROASTING

THE THING ABOUT STANDING IN FRONT OF A HOT OVEN ALL THE TIME IS THAT eventually you get hungry and start thinking about all the other things you could be cooking in this hot oven. Here are some of my favorites.

PASILLA AGRESIVO

chili

I have always imagined that a good bowl of chili should be based on a multiplicity of chiles, with no tomatoes to dilute their essence. One frigid winter day when I was working in the bakery and lamenting the dull gray skies outside, my thoughts turned to this imaginary chili bowl. I couldn't stop thinking about its heat and its flavors, and I finally rounded up a bunch of chile peppers and started cooking. The longer this chili cooks, the deeper and more devastatingly in agreement its flavors become. I like to cook it gently for at least 4 hours, but if you're in a pinch it is ready to eat after a 1-hour simmer.

> **Note:** We serve this chili by the cup in the café, and it has also become one of my favorite condiments—applied, for instance, to a breakfast egg, or spooned over a slice of truccio (page 93 or 97), and topped with a fried egg, grated cheese, and scallions.

YIELD: Serves 6   EQUIPMENT: A 4½-quart heavy-bottomed pot, a blender, and a mortar and pestle or spice grinder

1 medium red bell pepper

1 medium green bell pepper

1 or 2 fresh Fresno or other hot red chiles

1 large dried pasilla chile

300 grams (1⅓) cups robust red wine (a Merlot or Malbec works well)

2 teaspoons cumin seeds

454 grams (1 pound) lean ground sirloin

½ teaspoon ground Aleppo pepper (optional)

½ teaspoon red pepper flakes

1 medium onion, diced

1 medium celery rib, diced

1 small carrot, diced

300 grams (1¼ cups) water

One 15-ounce (425-gram) can black beans, undrained

2 bay leaves

1 heaping tablespoon dark chocolate chips

1. Heat the oven to 500°F. Roast the bell peppers and the Fresno chile in a pan for 15 to 20 minutes, until the skins bubble and char. Remove from the oven. Roast the pasilla pepper for just a few moments—until it puffs up and starts to smoke. Allow the peppers and chiles to

(CONTINUES)

cool. Remove the stems, skins, and seeds from the bell peppers. Remove only the stem and seeds from the Fresno chiles and pasilla pepper. Set aside.

2. Reduce the wine by half in a small saucepan over medium-high heat, and set aside. Toast the cumin seeds in a hot skillet over medium heat until fragrant. Finely grind the cumin seeds with a mortar and pestle or spice grinder. Set aside.

3. Place the peppers and chiles in a blender with the cooled reduced wine. Blend until smooth and set aside.

4. Combine the beef, cumin, Aleppo pepper (if using), and red pepper flakes in a 4½-quart heavy-bottomed pot over medium heat. Cook the beef, stirring occasionally, allowing the beef to form a nice brown crust, for 5 to 7 minutes. When the beef is deeply browned on the outside, add the onion, celery, and carrot. Cook, stirring occasionally, for 4 to 5 minutes or until the onion is soft. Add the blended peppers. Rinse the blender with the water and add this liquid to the pot. Add the beans and bay leaves and stir well. Sprinkle the chocolate chips over the chili. Bring the chili to a boil, reduce the heat, cover partially, and simmer for at least 1 hour. If desired, transfer the chili to a slow cooker and cook for 4 hours on high or 8 hours on low.

* eating

Serve with scallions or diced white onion, cilantro, lime, and sour cream.

PASTA AL FORNO
oven-baked pasta

I love making pasta al forno, especially in the winter. Often I take whatever I have around and bake it. Here are two favorite combinations.

FOR THE BÉCHAMEL:

YIELD: About 3 cups   EQUIPMENT: An 8-quart pot

70 grams (5 tablespoons) unsalted butter

20 grams (2 tablespoons) unbleached all-purpose flour

650 grams (3 cups) whole milk

2 grams (¼ teaspoon) fine sea salt

1 gram (¼ teaspoon) grated nutmeg

Melt the ½ stick of butter in a medium saucepan over high heat. Whisk in the flour and cook, whisking constantly until the flour is a light butterscotch color, about 2 minutes. Add the milk in a slow, steady stream, whisking continuously to keep lumps from forming. Keep whisking over high heat until the sauce begins to simmer. Add the salt and nutmeg and continue to whisk and cook for 5 minutes or until the sauce thickens and has the consistency of heavy cream. Pour the sauce into a bowl to cool.

FOR THE PASTA WITH ASPARAGUS AND CHARD:

YIELD: Serves 6 to 8   EQUIPMENT: One 2-quart baking dish

24 grams (2 tablespoons) coarse sea salt

454 grams (1 pound) dry rigatoni or penne pasta

1 bunch (½ pound/227 grams) chard, roughly chopped

1 bunch (½ pound/227 grams) asparagus, cut into 1-inch pieces

30 grams (2 tablespoons) extra virgin olive oil

6 cloves garlic, roughly chopped

1 batch béchamel (about 3 cups; see above)

130 grams (1½ cups) grated Parmigiano-Reggiano cheese

(CONTINUES)

1. Spread a tea towel on a sheet pan. Put about 6 quarts of water into an 8-quart pot, bring to a boil, and add the salt. Cook the pasta for the recommended time. Drain the pasta. Don't rinse it (unless you've overcooked it, in which case rinse immediately to stop the cooking!). Spread the pasta onto the sheet pan. Allow to cool. Heat the oven to 500°F.

2. Meanwhile, steam the chard and asparagus for 4 minutes or until tender. Heat the olive oil in a small skillet over high heat, add the garlic, and cook for a minute or so, until it begins to sizzle. Lower the heat and cook gently for another 3 to 4 minutes, until the garlic is browning lightly and is easily pierced with a fork. Remove from the heat and set aside.

3. Brush the casserole dish with a bit of the garlic olive oil. In a large bowl, combine the pasta, 2 teaspoons of the garlic oil, the béchamel, half of the grated cheese, and the steamed asparagus and chard until well incorporated. Pour the mixture into the casserole dish and top with the remaining cheese. Bake the casserole for 20 minutes or until the pasta begins to brown on top.

VARIATION

WITH PROSCIUTTO AND PEAS

YIELD: Serves 6 to 8   EQUIPMENT: One 2-quart baking dish

454 grams (1 pound) dry rigatoni or penne pasta

24 grams (2 tablespoons) coarse sea salt

10 grams (2 teaspoons) extra virgin olive oil plus 5 grams (1 teaspoon) for the baking dish

¾ cup diced onion

1 cup minced prosciutto or ham

140 grams (1 cup) fresh or frozen green peas

1 batch béchamel (about 3 cups; see above)

Freshly ground black pepper

130 grams (1½ cups) grated Parmigiano-Reggiano cheese

1 tablespoon dried bread crumbs

1. Spread a tea towel on a sheet pan. Put about 6 quarts of water into an 8-quart pot, bring to a boil, and add the salt. Cook the pasta for the recommended time. Drain the pasta. Don't rinse it (unless you've overcooked it, in which case rinse immediately to stop the cooking!). Spread the pasta onto the sheet pan. Allow to cool. Heat the oven to 500°F. Oil a 2-quart casserole and set aside.

2. Place 2 teaspoons of olive oil and the onion in a medium saucepan and cook over medium heat until the onion is just beginning to brown, 4 to 5 minutes. Add the prosciutto and cook for 2 to 3 minutes, stirring occasionally. Add the peas and cook for 1 to 2 minutes, until heated through. Transfer the prosciutto mixture to a large bowl and add the béchamel, black pepper to taste, pasta, and half of the grated cheese. Toss together and pour into the prepared baking dish. Combine the bread crumbs and remaining Parmigiano-Reggiano and scatter over the top. Bake for about 20 minutes, until the pasta browns lightly on top.

L'AMICO DI POLLO
roasted Japanese turnips

You may think a roast chicken has no better friend than the potato. These turnips may change your mind. The slight bit of sweetness, accentuated by the roasting, is alluring, and the comparative juiciness of the turnip helps tip the scale entirely. Hakurei turnips—sometimes called Japanese turnips—work best here; they are soft white turnips that can be quite small and are frequently found at farmers' markets from early summer through the late fall. At times they can be fantastically sweet and enjoyed raw, sliced, and unpeeled, much like an apple. If you use a larger variety of turnip, take care to find very fresh ones. Either cut them down to golf-ball-size pieces or increase the cooking time.

YIELD: Serves 2 to 4   EQUIPMENT: A large cast-iron skillet

1 bunch (250 grams/a little more than ½ pound) fresh turnips, preferably hakurei

15 grams (1 tablespoon) extra virgin olive oil

Salt

Put a large cast-iron skillet in the oven and heat to 500°F. Halve the turnips and toss them with the olive oil in a small bowl. Put the turnips, cut side down, into the hot skillet. Cook for about 10 minutes, until the turnips are soft on the inside and brown on the outside, with a little crunch around the edges. Toss with salt to taste when serving.

LE PATATE ARROSTO AL AGLIO

garlic roast potatoes

I used to know a baker named Remo, in San Casciano dei Bagni in Tuscany. When he wasn't baking, he would sling a rifle over his shoulder, hop onto his dirt bike, and ride out into the Tuscan hills. He would usually return with *lepre* (hare, or wild rabbit) and roast his lepre in the bread oven, next to a dish of rosemary potatoes and garlic. The lepre was intriguing, and the smell of rosemary was wonderful, but the real star was the garlic.

Here are Remo's garlic potatoes. The garlic is left in its skin to perfume the potatoes and also to keep the garlic from burning. When the potatoes are ready, serve the garlic cloves—still unpeeled—with the potatoes. To garlic lovers they are a treasure. For those without the inclination to squeeze the roasted garlic directly from peel to palate, discard the peels and spread the soft garlic on toast, with a generous drizzle of olive oil.

YIELD: Serves 4   EQUIPMENT: A 9-by-12-inch rimmed baking pan

800 grams (4 medium) new potatoes

8 medium garlic cloves, unpeeled

45 grams (3 tablespoons) extra virgin olive oil

1 sprig fresh rosemary

Dash of sweet paprika

Heat a roasting pan at 400°F. Peel the potatoes if you like them peeled, but don't peel the garlic! Toss the unpeeled garlic in 1 tablespoon of the olive oil in a small bowl and set aside. Cut the potatoes in half lengthwise and then in half again, also lengthwise, and then cut into 1-inch cubes as near in size to the cloves of garlic as you can make them. When the oven is heated, sprinkle the potatoes with the paprika and toss in the remaining 2 tablespoons of olive oil and the sprig of rosemary. Spread the potatoes and seasoning on the roasting pan as evenly as possible. Bake for 10 minutes and then add the garlic and oil on top. Roast for about 35 minutes longer. The potatoes are done when their tops have a golden crust and their bottoms are soft to the touch.

POLLO ARROSTO

roast chicken

There is a French dish called *poulet à la boulangère*, or "baker's chicken," which I cannot help thinking of every time I am starving and working in the bakery. Italian bakers are as likely to roast a rabbit as a chicken, but I am partial to chicken, and the idea is always the same: throw some supper in that hot bread oven! Village bakeries in Italy are organized along the lines of a very busy home kitchen; the oven tends to have pork roasts, sausages, rabbits, chickens—any or all of these things roasting or braising alongside the bread for the baker and his family to eat.

I suppose my time working in these bakeries has conditioned me to imagine that every bakery should have a chicken or two roasting near the bread. Or better yet, *on* the bread—one of the best improvements to a simple roast chicken is to sit it on top of six to eight large slices of bread. It is no exaggeration to say that the resulting bread—toasted from the heat of the oven, bathed in the juices of the roasting chicken—is one of life's greatest pleasures.

If you'd rather serve this with potatoes, the Garlic Roast Potatoes (page 171) work well, and they can roast alongside the chicken.

> **Note:** This roasted chicken is wonderful in the sandwich recipes in the following chapter.

YIELD: Serves 4 or 5   EQUIPMENT: Mortar and pestle

7 grams (1 tablespoon) finely grated fresh lemon zest

1 tablespoon fresh rosemary needles

2 garlic cloves (5 grams), chopped

1 teaspoon coarse sea salt

5 grams (1 teaspoon) fresh lemon juice

20 grams (1 tablespoon) anchovy paste or 6 anchovy fillets packed in oil

3 grams (¾ teaspoon) freshly ground black pepper

40 grams (½ cup) extra virgin olive oil

1 whole chicken (1.3 to 1.8 kilograms/ 3 to 4 pounds)

1. With a mortar and pestle, crush the lemon zest, rosemary, garlic, and salt into a paste. Add the lemon juice and pound in the anchovy, then add the black pepper and olive oil. Dry the chicken thoroughly. Rub the marinade into the inside and all over the outside of the chicken. Allow the chicken to sit at room temperature for 30 minutes. (If you have time, refrigerate for 1 to 2 hours, and then bring back to room temperature for 30 minutes.)

2. Heat the oven to 500°F. Line the bottom of a shallow roasting pan with parchment paper or aluminum foil to prevent the chicken from sticking when you flip it. Put the chicken breast side down on the parchment. Roast the chicken for 15 minutes. Remove the pan from the oven. Using tongs, carefully flip the chicken over onto its back, taking the parchment with it, directly onto the roasting pan. The chicken will be hot, but not too hot to handle. Discard the parchment or foil. Turn the oven down to 425°F. (If you are roasting the potatoes, put them in now, and they will be done at the same time.)

3. Return the pan to the oven and roast the chicken for another 45 to 50 minutes or until the skin is perfectly crisp, there are clear juices flowing from the bird, and the internal temperature of the thigh is 165°F. Let rest under a foil tent for 10 to 15 minutes before carving.

VARIATION

Here is a similar rub with lavender. If you don't have fresh lavender, fresh tarragon works nicely as well.

- **1 large garlic clove (5 grams)**
- **5 grams (1 tablespoon) fresh lavender or tarragon**
- **5 grams (1 teaspoon) fine sea salt**
- **5 grams (1 teaspoon) cider vinegar**
- **20 grams (1 tablespoon) anchovy paste or 6 anchovy fillets packed in oil**
- **10 grams (2 teaspoons) dry mustard**
- **½ teaspoon sweet paprika**
- **1 gram (¼ teaspoon) freshly ground black pepper**
- **15 grams (1 tablespoon) extra virgin olive oil**

With a mortar and pestle, crush the garlic, lavender, and salt until the lavender leaves are broken up and the garlic is mashed. Add the vinegar and pound in the anchovy paste, then add the mustard, paprika, black pepper, and, finally, the olive oil. Rub the marinade all over the dried chicken as directed and proceed with the recipe.

PUNTA DI PETTO DI TÈ

brisket braised in black tea

In 2012, I went to Turkmenistan on a diplomatic mission. I had been asked to instruct local culinary students in my baking methods and to cook Thanksgiving dinner for the U.S. Embassy. I was excited to do both of these things, but I do not have a diplomatic temperament. In fact, many of those who know me best worried I'd end up in a Turkmenian jail after inadvertently or advertently insulting my hosts. Turkmenistan was formerly part of the USSR and is not as permissive as the average Western democracy. It is also a predominately Muslim country, and alcohol of any kind is officially forbidden.

I was intrigued by the constraints of cooking without wine, and when I came back to New York, I decided to try a Turkmen-inspired braise using tea rather than wine. I made a pot of strong black tea, added some spices that seemed friendly to a spice route braise (star anise, ginger, Sichuan peppercorns), and cooked a fine brisket in the resulting tea for a very, very long time. The result was sublime. The delicate spices and mellow notes of the tea allowed the slow-cooked beefy flavors to rule the dish in the most luscious way.

I like using brisket because it has a terrific flavor that braises well. Choose a brisket that still has the cap of fat around the meat and leave it on as it cooks; it will add tremendous flavor to the meat as it braises. This is a long-cooking but wonderfully easy dish to make—after giving the meat a quick sear, you put everything in a pot and let the long, slow braise of 12 to 14 hours do all the work. If you're not comfortable cooking the meat overnight, as I do, you could start it first thing in the morning and have it ready for dinner.

YIELD: Serves 8 to 10 people as an entrée or makes about 12 Braised Brisket Sandwiches with Slaw (page 188)
EQUIPMENT: A 6-quart or larger pot with a lid

4 English Breakfast black tea bags

8 whole cloves

4 whole star anise

¼ cup Szechuan peppercorns*

1 large leek, split lengthwise and cut into 4-inch pieces

  * It is worth seeking these out for their piney flavor and explosive zing. Sometimes your local Chinese restaurant will help you out by giving you a little packet of these. Eaten raw, they are mouth-numbing, but cooked, they deliver a mellow pop. If you can't find any, you could substitute a mixture of 3 to 4 juniper berries and 3 to 4 allspice berries.

1 medium onion, peeled and halved lengthwise

4 medium carrots, peeled and split lengthwise

4 pitted dates

¼ cup peeled fresh ginger cut into ½-inch chunks

1 tablespoon honey

2 to 4 whole dried small red chiles

3 bay leaves

One 4- to 6-pound beef brisket, untrimmed, with fat cap still attached

24 grams (2 tablespoons) coarse sea salt

1. Fill a pot large enough to hold the brisket half full of water (about a quart) and bring to a boil over medium-high heat. Add the tea bags and steep for 6 minutes. Remove and discard the tea bags. (Do not squeeze them out.) Heat a small skillet over high heat. When it is blazing hot, toss in the cloves, star anise, and peppercorns and quickly toast for about 20 seconds, shaking the skillet a bit to prevent sticking. A little smoke is okay, but don't let them burn—remove from the heat once you smell them. Add the toasted spices to the tea and then the leek, onion, carrots, dates, ginger, honey, chiles to taste, and bay leaves.

2. Bring the liquid to a boil and then turn off the heat. Heat the oven to 225°F. Heat a very large frying pan, roasting pan, or skillet—larger than the largest flat side of the brisket—over medium-high heat. Put the brisket straight into the hot skillet, fat side down. Cook both flat sides for about 4 minutes each, to give a light sear. Hold up the brisket with tongs to sear any remaining sides for an additional 4 minutes—depending on how your brisket is cut, it may be in the shape of a triangle or a square.

3. Place the seared brisket into the pot of hot tea so the fat side is on the surface of the tea. Sprinkle the salt on this side. Cover the pot and cook for 12 to 14 hours.

(CONTINUES)

Braised brisket and
brisket sandwiches
(page 188).

4. Once the brisket has finished cooking, it will have a nice dark crust and the fat will be amber colored with a golden crust. Use tongs to remove the brisket while the brine is still hot. Set it on a plate or in a pan. Allow it to cool, covered with a piece of foil.

5. There may be as much as an inch or two of fat floating on the surface of the liquid in the pot. Carefully ladle it out and discard. Strain out the vegetables and spices and discard. This broth will be your sauce. It is ambrosial: a rich, meaty broth perfumed with the warmth and sweetness of the steeped tea and spices.

> **Notes:** If you make this in advance of serving, I recommend that when you do serve it, cut the brisket into slices first and warm them up in a skillet, so that you can heat them through gently on each side. Warm up the braising liquid separately and serve each slice of brisket with a ladle of sauce.
>
> This recipe produces ample broth. I recommend enjoying a cup of warm broth with a thick slice of Pane Pugliese (page 76) or Pane Bianco (page 89) and plenty of butter.

✳ eating

Serve slices of the brisket with a generous spoonful of sauce. For sides, keep it classic and serve with boiled potatoes and mustard greens. Or consider the approach of legendary Italian butcher Dario Cecchini, who serves some of the finest steaks in Italy with fennel, carrot, and celery sticks—the idea being that the clean crunch of the raw vegetables will complement the rich, potent flavors of the meat. Certainly thick slices of bread are required here, no matter what.

ROAST BEEF WITH SMOKED PAPRIKA

There is nothing Italian about this roast. It is just simple, quick, and beautiful. If you have some remaining after dinner, serve thin slices of this cold, for lunch, or layer a bit on a sandwich for the Panini di Manzo (page 190).

YIELD: Serves 8 to 10   EQUIPMENT: Meat thermometer

One 5- to 7-pound beef eye of round roast, trussed

4 to 5 tablespoons hot Spanish pimentón (smoked paprika)

1. Heat the oven to 400°F with a rack in the middle. Lightly oil a wire rack that fits into a sheet pan and set aside.

2. Place the beef on a sheet of parchment paper or other disposable surface (the paprika can stain!) and consider wearing disposable gloves to avoid staining your hands. Shake the paprika directly out of the canister over the meat, turning the beef as you go, until every surface is bright scarlet.

3. Put the meat thermometer into one end of the roast and put the roast, fat side up, onto the wire rack on the sheet pan. Roast for 30 minutes, then flip the meat over. Cook for another 30 minutes or until the internal temperature reaches 120°F.

4. Remove the roast from the oven on the sheet pan and use aluminum foil to make a tent over the meat. Leave the thermometer in and you will see that the internal temperature rises to 128° to 130°F, as the meat continues to cook, and then begins to decline. Once the temperatures goes back down to 120°F—this will take about 30 minutes—the roast is ready to serve. It will be perfectly medium-rare. Serve with Garlic Roast Potatoes (page 171) and Tomato and Arugula Salad (page 194).

Chicken club sandwich (page 187) on Pullman slices.

8

SANDWICHES, SALADS, AND CONDIMENTS

SANDWICHES

SOME OF THE SANDWICHES HERE REQUIRE JUST SIMPLE ASSEMBLY. OTHERS— our reigning favorites from the café—are more obsessive affairs. The everything-but-the-kitchen-sink free-for-all goes against all of my mantras about doing more with less, but our breads are so simple that it is extraordinarily fun to go crazy with our sandwich fillings, and they have become such a draw at the café that we end up selling more sandwiches than bread—which is not what I set out to do!

In the café, we use pizza bianca (pages 65 and 118), sliced open like a pita, for nearly every sandwich. Throughout these recipes, I suggest other breads from the book that match well with the sandwich fillings, but I encourage you to use any bread that you've made—there is nothing more satisfying than serving a sandwich on bread that you have made yourself.

PANINI DI CECI

chickpea fritter and tahini sandwiches

I've been eating falafel since I first came to New York City in 1984. I may operate an Italian-inspired café, but I love falafel, and this sandwich is one of our best sellers. It is the perfect place to exercise some artistic license. We often add a mix of crisp seasonable vegetables: chunks of fresh cucumber, a handful of mesclun, a few roasted beets, a bit of dill or cilantro. In winter we might use a few thin slices of orange with fresh mint. If you have any handy, Quick-Pickled Fennel (page 196) or Red Onions (page 195) always work well on this sandwich, as does a drizzle of some spicy sauce like harissa or Lacto-Fermented Chile Peppers (page 198). A cucumber pickle (page 200) sliced into the mix always works well.

If you are at a loss for where to start with so many possibilities, I recommend a simple shepherd's salad: chopped tomatoes, cucumber, and onion with a few leaves of lettuce and a handful of parsley and cilantro. No matter how you choose to top your fritters, be sure to pack them into a Whole Wheat Pita (page 105) and add plenty of tahini.

YIELD: 4 large sandwiches   EQUIPMENT: A food processor or blender and a thermometer or deep fryer
PLAN AHEAD: Soak the chickpeas overnight. Prepare the pita if using.

175 grams (1 cup) dried chickpeas

100 grams (½ cup) grated onion

8 grams (2 tablespoons) chopped fresh cilantro

4 grams (1 teaspoon) peeled, grated fresh ginger

1 teaspoon fine sea salt, plus a pinch for the sauce

1 gram (½ teaspoon) freshly ground black pepper

0.5 gram (⅛ teaspoon) baking soda

Pinch of Aleppo pepper or smoked sweet paprika

2 cups canola oil for deep frying

45 to 60 grams (3 to 4 tablespoons) water, or more as needed

2 tablespoons tahini

1 teaspoon fresh lemon juice

4 big handfuls mesclun

Ground dried sumac (optional)

4 Whole Wheat Pitas (page 105)

1. Soak the chickpeas in 375 grams (1⅔ cups) of water for 8 hours. Split open the chickpea skins in a blender or food processor. If using a blender, pour the chickpeas and all their water, plus an additional 800 to 900 grams (about 4 cups) of water, into the blender. Pulse very briefly at a low speed, moving the chickpeas around from time to time, until all the

(CONTINUES)

chickpeas are cracked and in large pieces. (If using a food processor, drain the water from the soaking chickpeas. Pulse just enough times to crack open the chickpeas.) Once all the chickpeas appear to be cracked open, put the chickpeas into a very large bowl and fill it with water. Swish the water around with your hands, and the translucent chickpea skins will float to the top of the water and the chickpeas will sink. Pour off the water with the skins. Repeat as needed with fresh water until you've removed as much of the floating skins as possible. You can also use a mesh strainer to catch the skins as they float in the water. (Removing the skins ensures the chickpeas will stick together; this is also the trick to making silky hummus.) Drain the chickpeas in a colander and allow to sit for 30 minutes to dry, stirring occasionally to remove the excess water.

2. Place the drained chickpeas in a large bowl and add the onion, cilantro, ginger, salt, black pepper, baking soda, and Aleppo pepper and stir to combine. Transfer the chickpeas to the blender or food processor. Pulse until the chickpeas are broken up into small chunks. Test to see whether they are small and crushed enough by taking a handful to see if it will hold a ball. If it doesn't, pulse a few more times. Test again and stop blending as soon as you find that they are "ballable." Once the chickpea mixture is ready, cover and let rest at room temperature or in the refrigerator for about 2 hours and up to 8 hours.

3. Use a regular tablespoon from the silverware drawer to scoop out one fritter at a time. Turn the spoonful of chickpeas into the palm of your hand and use the spoon to pat and press the fritter into an oval shape. Gently squeeze out any excess moisture as you form the fritters. Set the fritters down on a plate or some parchment paper as you make them. You should have about 16 small fritters.

4. Line a sheet pan with paper towels and top with a wire rack. Heat 2 cups of oil in a deep saucepan or deep fryer to 375°F. (Make sure the height of the saucepan is at least double the height of the oil, in case the oil bubbles up during frying.) Use a slotted spoon or basket to lower in three fritters at a time. Allow the fritters to cook for 2 to 3 minutes or until deeply browned, turning them occasionally as they float to the top. Drain on the rack.

5. Use a spoon to mix the water with the tahini until the tahini emulsifies and thickens. Keep adding water, a tablespoon at a time, and the tahini will thin out and then thicken once again. Keep drizzling in water until the tahini turns white and creamy, like a thick pancake batter. Add a pinch of salt and the lemon juice.

6. Put three or four chickpea fritters in each pita round and add a drizzle of tahini, a hefty spoonful of your other favorite vegetables, another drizzle of tahini, a handful of mesclun or other greens, and a dash of sumac if you have it. Serve immediately.

PANINI DI POLLO POSTMODERNO

chicken, avocado, and kimchi sandwiches

Here's a chicken sandwich in which the creaminess comes not from the usual suspect (mayonnaise), but from an avocado. I came up with it when we were roasting a lot of chicken in our bread oven at the café, and my wife had been working for Hawthorne Valley Farm—a biodynamic farm in New York that makes a spectacular, idiosyncratic version of kimchi. It is colorful, garlicky, and completely nontraditional: a rainbow of radish ribbons, carrot strips, pepper flakes, and salty cabbage slivers. It went perfectly with avocado, and I decided to make a sandwich with kimchi, avocado, and chicken. The sour, salty spice of kimchi is a crisp complement to cold roast chicken, and the avocado tempers the tartness, rounds out the flavors, and yokes them together. This combination works well with traditional kimchi as well; if you want to try Hawthorne Valley's, order it at farmtopeople.com.

YIELD: 4 sandwiches

¼ cup mayonnaise

8 slices bread—Pugliese (page 76) and Multigrani (page 99) are both particularly good here

3 cups shredded or pulled Roast Chicken (page 172), white and dark meat

1 big handful mesclun

1 cup kimchi

1 ripe avocado, pitted, peeled, and thinly sliced

Use a generous teaspoon of mayonnaise on the bottom slices of bread. Add ¾ cup of roast chicken per sandwich, a good handful of mesclun, and layer on about ¼ cup of kimchi per sandwich. Top the kimchi with three or four slices of avocado and then add the top slices of bread. Slice in half and serve.

Chicken club sandwich, cut in quarters.

TRAMEZZINI DI POLLO

chicken club sandwiches

This triple-decker sandwich is our take on a classic club sandwich. It is my idea of the perfect marriage of flavor and texture: each bite is creamy, crunchy, and aromatic. There is nothing Italian about the flavors, but the form—a tramezzini, or three-level bite—is an Italian favorite.

YIELD: 4 triple-decker sandwiches
EQUIPMENT: Long toothpicks—the more decorative and over the top, the better—to hold these sandwiches together
PLAN AHEAD: Have 2 loaves of sandwich bread ready.

8 thin slices prosciutto (about ¼ pound/113 grams)

12 slices of square-shaped sandwich bread such as Pane al Latte (page 58), crusts removed

½ cup mayonnaise

2½ teaspoons smoked Spanish paprika

½ cup soft goat cheese, such as chèvre

½ cup thinly sliced roasted red peppers

2 cups shredded or pulled Roast Chicken (page 172), white and dark meat

16 large fresh basil leaves

Quick-Pickled Fennel (page 196)

1. Heat the oven to 400°F. Place the slices of prosciutto on a sheet pan. Place the bread on a separate sheet pan. Bake together until crispy, 10 or 11 minutes. Meanwhile, combine the mayonnaise and paprika and set aside.

2. Line up the toast slices on a work surface so that they are three high and four across. This will help you keep track of which slices are on the bottom, in the middle, and on top. Slather all the top and bottom slices with a layer of paprika mayonnaise. Put a thin spread of goat cheese on the middle slices. Top with a few pieces of roasted red pepper.

3. Cover each bottom slice with ¼ cup of chicken and a prosciutto crisp. Put the middle slice on top of the prosciutto, red pepper side up. Add ¼ cup of chicken and another piece of prosciutto. Top with four basil leaves, a teaspoon of pickled fennel, and the top slice of bread (mayonnaise side down). Secure the sandwiches with a toothpick or skewer. Slice each sandwich in half diagonally and serve.

PANINI DI PETTO

braised brisket sandwiches with slaw

Yes, it is worth braising a brisket just to make this sandwich. I made a braise that tastes like a sizzling backyard porterhouse hot off a summertime grill—and I put it on a sandwich. The result is divine. The flavor is richly beefy. The slaw on top is fresh and crispy to complement the big umami flavors of the beef.

YIELD: 12 sandwiches

PLAN AHEAD: Have 2 loaves Pane Pugliese (page 76) or Ciabatta (page 85) ready. Bring the brisket to room temperature. Set aside the braising liquid.

½ cup grated carrot

2 cups thinly sliced red or green cabbage

½ cup thinly sliced celery or celery root

½ cup thinly sliced red onion

2 tablespoons roughly chopped fresh parsley

1 teaspoon caraway seeds, toasted

1 tablespoon extra virgin olive oil

3 tablespoons cider vinegar

2 teaspoons fine sea salt, plus more as needed

¼ teaspoon freshly ground black pepper

Brisket Braised in Black Tea (page 174) plus 3 cups of the reduced braising liquid

24 slices Pane Pugliese (page 76) or Ciabatta (page 85)

½ cup mayonnaise

1. Grate the carrot on the large holes of a box grater and place in a large bowl with the cabbage, celery, onion, parsley and caraway seeds. Toss with the oil, vinegar, salt, and pepper and set aside. Heat the oven to 500°F.

2. Thinly slice the brisket—¼ inch to ½ inch thick—or shred by hand. Set aside. Toast the bread. (If you are making a dozen sandwiches at once, toast the bread in the oven, on one side only: lay flat on a sheet pan and toast for 4 to 5 minutes.) Slather the bread with mayonnaise. Bring the braising liquid to a boil in a small pot and then turn it off, leaving the pot on the burner to retain heat. You want the braising liquid to be hot enough to heat up the meat. Use a slotted spoon to dip slices or hunks of meat into the juice for about 5 seconds per slice—and then spoon the meat and juice directly onto the bread. You may want to drain off some of the juice, or not, depending on your tastes. Add a big spoonful of slaw to each sandwich. Add salt to taste and enjoy.

Braised brisket sandwich with slaw on ciabatta.

PANINI DI MANZO

roast beef sandwiches with spicy mayo

This sandwich is light on the beef and layered with crunchy, aromatic vegetables.

YIELD: 4 sandwiches

½ cup mayonnaise

¼ cup Lacto-Fermented Chile Peppers (page 198) or other hot sauce

8 slices bread or 4 wedges Pizza Bianca (page 65 or 118), sliced open like clamshells

16 to 20 very thin slices Roast Beef with Smoked Paprika (page 179)

Salt

8 tablespoons of Quick-Pickled Red Onions (page 195)

1 large seedless cucumber, sliced thinly lengthwise to fit the bread

1 heaping cup fresh cilantro, leaves and tender sprigs only

Stir together the mayonnaise and hot sauce. Spread each bottom slice of the bread with about 2 teaspoons of the spicy mayo. Layer 4 to 5 thin slices of roast beef on top and salt the beef lightly. Top the beef with pickled red onions, a few long, thin slices of cucumber, and a handful of fresh cilantro. Close the sandwiches and serve.

SALADS AND CONDIMENTS

A BREAD-BASED DIET ALWAYS NEEDS GREENS. MY SALADS ARE DECIDEDLY bread-friendly: once you've finished eating your salad, you'll probably want to take a piece of bread and wipe the plate clean. My dressings always aim for a base of acidity, a smooth finish of olive oil, and a solid, savory punch from a little aged cheese or pickled onion or a pinch of anchovy.

There are condiments in this chapter as well—some for salads or sandwiches, and some, like the lacto-fermented chile peppers (page 198), that might be used anywhere. Several of the condiments are lacto-fermented. I love pickling things in this manner because—like making bread with natural leavening—it is another ancient kind of fermentation. Contrary to what the name suggests, lacto-fermentation has nothing to do with milk. The *lacto* refers to a type of bacteria, *lactobacilli* (lactic acid bacteria), that are found on nearly all vegetables. When lactic acid bacteria are provided with the right ingredients (vegetables, salt, time, and cool weather), they multiply and preserve the product in question by creating an environment too acidic for anything else to survive. This kind of fermentation is the method used to preserve dietary staples all over the world—from sauerkraut to kimchi. At root, it is a way of storing vegetables without requiring vinegar or canning—but I favor it because it makes scrumptious flavors and, of course, I love to ferment.

Apple-celery salad.

APPLE-CELERY SALAD

This salad was inspired by an unusual variety of apple I found at the Union Square Farmers' Market. Called "goldrush," they are a lovely yellow-bronze color, pleasantly tart, and exceptionally firm. They are perfect for salad because they hold up to a little bit of dressing and tossing and their tartness stands out amid the other flavors. If you cannot find this particular variety, use the firmest, tartest apples available.

YIELD: Serves 4

28 grams (1 ounce) sunflower seeds

350 grams (about 7 ribs) celery

2 firm, tart apples (250 grams)

25 grams leek, thinly sliced into half-moons (about ¼ cup)

25 grams (about ½ bunch) fresh parsley, chopped

Salt and freshly ground pepper

36 grams (2⅓ tablespoons) extra virgin olive oil

1 large radish—I like black radishes and watermelon radishes here (optional)

1. Toast the sunflower seeds in a pan until golden, crunchy, and fragrant. (A little char is nice, but take care not to burn them.)

2. Slice the celery on the bias into long thin strips. Quarter and core the apples and slice thinly. Combine the celery, apples, toasted seeds, leeks, and parsley in a large bowl. Grate the radish, if using, directly into the bowl. When ready to serve, season with salt and pepper to taste and dress with the olive oil.

TOMATO AND ARUGULA SALAD

It helps to have really beautiful tomatoes for this—that hard-to-find perfect balance of sweetness, acidity, firmness, and umami.

YIELD: Serves 2 to 4

100 grams (6 cups tightly packed) arugula

100 grams tomatoes, cut into wedges (¾ cup)

40 grams (½ cup packed) Quick-Pickled Red Onions (page 195)

30 grams (3 tablespoons) extra virgin olive oil

5 grams (heaping ½ cup) cilantro leaves

3 grams (½ teaspoon) fine sea salt

Toss everything together in a large bowl. Eat!

QUICK-PICKLED RED ONIONS

With a little olive oil, these red onions make spectacular salad dressing. They are also an excellent addition to sandwiches.

YIELD: 1½ cups   EQUIPMENT: A glass or ceramic container with a cover

1 medium red onion, peeled and thinly sliced

300 grams (1⅓ cups) rice wine or white vinegar

5 grams (1 teaspoon) sugar

3 grams (½ teaspoon) noniodized fine sea salt

8 juniper berries

Place the onion in a glass or ceramic container. Heat the vinegar in a small pot with the sugar, salt, and juniper berries. When the vinegar reaches a boil, pour it over the onions. Cover and cool; they will turn pink as they steep. Use immediately or store, covered, in the refrigerator for up to a month.

QUICK-PICKLED FENNEL

Pickled fennel can be wonderful on sandwiches (such as the chicken club on page 187), and is also delicious in salads or as an accompaniment to roasted meats. Its native habitat, however, may be on a cheese plate, particularly one that features prosciutto, salumi, and olives.

YIELD: 2 cups   EQUIPMENT: Glass or ceramic container with a lid

1 large fennel bulb (250 grams)

300 grams (1¼ cups) rice wine or white vinegar

5 grams (1 teaspoon) sugar

3 grams (½ teaspoon) noniodized fine sea salt

Remove the stalk and root from the fennel bulb and use a knife or mandoline to slice it about ⅛ inch thick. Place the fennel in a small glass or ceramic bowl. Bring the vinegar, sugar, and salt to a boil in a small saucepan. Stir to dissolve the sugar and then pour the vinegar over the fennel. If the fennel isn't completely covered, that's fine—the fennel will slip below the surface as it cools. Allow to cool completely and then eat or refrigerate, covered, for up to a month.

ORIGINAL MUSTARD
lacto-fermented mustard

Humans and mustard seeds go way back—it's one of the most ancient grains that we've gathered and cultivated. I wanted to imagine what mustard tasted like before the industrial revolution, and so I started making my own. There is such a complexity of flavor in the fermentation of a mustard seed, an astonishing spectrum of aromas: hot, spicy, musky—and laden with umami. You will find the brown seeds much more pungent than the yellow.

YIELD: 1 quart; 0.9 kilogram   EQUIPMENT: A 1-quart mason jar, sterilized in boiling water or a dishwasher

750 grams (3½ cups) distilled or boiled tap water, cooled to room temperature

26 grams (2 tablespoons) noniodized fine sea salt

200 grams (scant 1 cup) yellow or brown mustard seeds

1. Dissolve the salt into the water in a 1-quart mason jar. Add the mustard seeds and stir. There should be about an inch of water above the seeds. Let sit, covered loosely, at room temperature, for a day.

2. When a day goes by, if there are still mustard seeds floating at the top, and they don't stir back in, remove them with a spoon. Leave at room temperature (65° to 70°F), loosely covered (you want air to circulate and gas to escape). The seeds will cling together, and you'll notice that in 2 to 4 days bubbles will form. It's a sign fermentation has begun. You can let it go longer—up to 6 days—or you can refrigerate (or store someplace else cool) once bubbles appear.

3. You can eat it right away, but I like to refrigerate it and wait a month for the flavors to mature. By that time it will smell a lot like a pickle barrel (you may notice there are a lot of mustard seeds in pickles!). Pour the entire contents of the jar into a blender and blend until smooth. (If it still seems too thick, thin to the desired consistency by adding distilled water.) Put in a clean jar, refrigerate, and use within 6 months.

LACTO-FERMENTED CHILE PEPPERS

natural sriracha

This makes the most wonderful, addictive hot sauce in the world. It is always found on our dinner table at home, and we go through so many of these chile peppers at the café that we began fermenting them by the bucketful. The heat level depends on the variety of chile pepper that you use—I prefer red Thai finger chiles or fresh cherry peppers. Habaneros tend to be too spicy. At home we eat these with scrambled eggs or add a drizzle to chicken soup or a heaping spoonful to black beans and rice. At the bakery, this condiment is essential to our capicola pizza (page 121). I think of it as natural sriracha.

YIELD: 1 quart   EQUIPMENT: A 1-quart mason jar, sterilized in boiling water or a dishwasher

1 kilogram (about 2¼ pounds) very fresh spicy chiles, preferably red Thai finger chiles

33 grams (2 generous tablespoons) noniodized sea salt

10 grams (2 teaspoons) peeled, grated ginger

1 garlic clove, chopped

Trim off the stems from the chiles, remove the white piths, and, if you prefer to lower the heat, remove the seeds. Quarter the chiles and place all the ingredients in a food processor. Pulse for 15 seconds or until they are the size you like (keep in mind that chunky works better for fermentation). Transfer to a wide-mouth, quart-size mason jar, and use a sterilized small ceramic dish to weigh down the pulp below any liquid that emerges. Cover loosely and allow to sit at room temperature for 2 to 5 days or until you notice many tiny little bubbles forming. Eat now or refrigerate and wait 1 to 2 months for the flavors to develop (I recommend the latter course of action). These chiles will keep, covered, for up to 4 months in the refrigerator.

Lacto-fermented chile peppers.

CETRIOLI

lacto-fermented cucumber pickles

This is the old-fashioned way to make pickles: no vinegar, just time and brine. The lactic acid bacteria on the skin of the cucumbers gradually sour the brine and the cucumbers, so the longer the cucumbers pickle, the more sour they become.

I find that the sourness of a naturally fermented pickle to be quite different from the acidity of a vinegar pickle—to me the juices of the cucumber are more prominent here since they are not competing with the strength of the acetic acid in the vinegar.

The secret to making amazing pickles is to find the freshest organic cucumbers possible. Kirby cucumbers of course work well, but I also like Persian cucumbers because they have small seeds and are particularly crispy. Either way, to ensure a fine and crispy pickle batch, try to find and use cucumbers no more than 3 days old and make sure your surfaces are sterile and the water in your brine pure or distilled.

YIELD: 1 quart   EQUIPMENT: A 1-quart mason jar, sterilized in boiling water or a dishwasher

26 grams (2 tablespoons) noniodized sea salt

About 2 cups distilled or boiled tap water, cooled to room temperature

1 garlic clove

½ teaspoon dill seeds

¼ teaspoon brown mustard seeds

Fresh dill flowers (optional)

454 grams (1 pound) just-picked 5-inch-long Kirby cucumbers, lightly rinsed

1 bay leaf

1. Dissolve the salt in the water in a medium bowl. Add the garlic, dill seeds, and mustard seeds. If you have fresh dill flowers, add those too. Set this bowl aside.

2. Use a very clean knife and cutting board to quarter the cucumbers lengthwise. Press them into the jar until you can't squeeze any more in. Wedge a large bay leaf into the side of the jar. Add the brine to cover them. Cover the jar loosely.

3. The cucumbers may start to drift up in the brine, above the water. If they do, find something heavy that fits in the jar, ensure it's extremely clean, and use it to weigh down the cucumbers.

4. Let the pickles sit at room temperature for up to 3 days—I usually refrigerate mine when I see that fermentation has started, indicated by the presence of a few small bubbles at the top. There is no wrong time to eat these pickles, but I recommend trying to wait until they've been in the brine under refrigeration for at least 2 weeks. They taste best after a month or more.

POMODORI SECCHI AL FORNO

oven-dried tomatoes

These are cooked for a long time at a low heat so that they simply dry out. In removing the tomatoes' moisture, this process brings out their tart, sweet essence. I prefer to use Roma or San Marzano types of plum tomatoes, but other varieties will also work. Try to find tomatoes that are very ripe and also somewhat tart. (The round hothouse-grown tomatoes often found in the grocery store, for instance, are often beautiful but tend not to have enough acidity to succeed in this recipe.)

YIELD: 1 pint   EQUIPMENT: Two 1-pint glass jars with lids

2 kilograms (4½ pounds) large plum tomatoes, such as Roma

24 grams (2 tablespoons) coarse sea salt

About 300 grams (1 to 1½ cups) extra virgin olive oil

1 sprig fresh rosemary or thyme (optional)

1. Heat the oven to 180° to 200°F. Cut the tomatoes in half lengthwise. Snuggle the tomatoes close together on a sheet pan, cut side up. Sprinkle about ¼ teaspoon of the salt into each tomato. Bake for 9 to 10 hours, until the tomatoes have shrunk by about 75 percent— and are very dark in color. The texture will be much like that of sun-dried tomatoes, but a bit juicier.

2. Fill the jars with the tomatoes and add enough olive oil so that the tomatoes are submerged. If you have a sprig of fresh rosemary or thyme, break it in two and add a piece to each jar. Cover and store in the refrigerator for 2 or 3 months. Either rinse or pat off the oil from the tomatoes when you are ready to use them.

Dusting focaccia fiorentina (page 223)
with confectioners' sugar.

9

DOLCI

I LIKE ITALIAN DESSERTS BECAUSE THEY ARE SIMPLE, QUICK, AND ELEGANT.
Like a tip of the hat to the pleasures of the table before heading down the lane, Italian
desserts are as ephemeral as they are civilized. There is also an enlightened ambiguity
that unites and enlivens the Italian categories of dessert, afternoon treat, and breakfast. I admire this confusion; in my own perfect world there will always be a pinch of
something special and sweet to start the day with, alongside a strong and steaming
mug of coffee. I have named this chapter *dolci*—which means "sweets"—because
everything in it is a bit sugary and will most likely strike you as a dessert. But these
tarts, cookies, and cakes could quite rightfully appear on the table throughout the day,
just as many of my favorite breakfast items—such as the Torta d'Olio d'Oliva (Orange
Olive-Oil cake, page 142), or Bomboloni (Italian doughnuts, page 153)—are desserts
in disguise.

SCOZZESE

shortbread cookies

As a child I loved the Danish butter cookies that come in a big blue tin and show up in grocery stores around Christmas. As an adult, my confectionary interests shaped up a bit and I developed a particular affection for Walker's Shortbread. After spending a small fortune on weekly boxes of these Scottish imports, I finally thought: maybe I should just make these myself?

Some people prefer their shortbread very pale, but I like to bake these until they brown around the edges. The sugar in the cookies never gets hot enough to caramelize, but the sugars in the wheat do, and the flavors created by the toasting flour and browning butter are—to me—irresistible. We make these at the bakery in several versions, and I give them all here: plain, chocolate, and spice (in the tradition of Dutch speculoos). We call them all *scozzese*, which is Italian for Scottish.

YIELD: 10 to 12 small cookies
EQUIPMENT: A 10-inch tart pan with a removable bottom or a 9-inch metal pie pan or a parchment-lined baking sheet

150 grams (1 cup) unbleached all-purpose flour

50 grams (¼ cup) sugar

3 grams (½ teaspoon) fine sea salt

113 grams (1 stick/8 tablespoons) top-quality unsalted butter, cut into small pieces and softened

1. Heat the oven to 400°F. Stir the flour, sugar, and salt together with a fork in a medium bowl. Add the softened butter and mix with the fork. Mix until the ingredients are well combined, but note that the dough will not come together on its own. It should be crumbly. Use your hands to gently squeeze the dough into a loose ball and then knead lightly until the dough is quite malleable. Press the dough into the tart pan in a nice even layer or pat the dough into a giant cookie—square, circle, or rectangle—about ½ inch thick. Use your favorite cookie cutters, or bake as is.

2. Bake for 18 to 20 minutes or until the shortbread has turned a lovely golden hue, slightly darker around the edges. Using a sharp knife, cut the shortbread into 12 wedges. Place the pan on a cooling rack. When cool, carefully cut through the wedges again and remove the shortbread from the pan.

(CONTINUES)

SCOZZESE NERO
chocolate shortbread cookies

Add 25 grams (3 tablespoons) unsweetened dark cocoa powder to the dry ingredients and proceed as directed.

SPECULOOS
spiced shortbread cookies

Add to the dry ingredients 0.5 gram (¼ teaspoon) each ground green cardamom, freshly ground black pepper, ground ginger, and ground cinnamon and proceed as directed.

> **Note:** This recipe uses what I consider to be a baker's most basic units of measure: a stick of butter and a cup of flour. I love the symmetry of this relationship, and I also like that it makes just enough cookies to satisfy a late-night craving. If you'd like to make more, simply double or triple the recipe. The cookies store well, in a tightly sealed container, for several months.

CAPRINO

goat cheese and rhubarb cookies

Early one spring, when rhubarb and goat cheese were some of the few things in abundance at our New York farmers' markets, a former Sullivan Street pastry chef, Ashley Whitmore, came up with these cookies. We named them *caprino* after the goat cheese that gives these cookies the nicest bit of tartness. If you don't have rhubarb, these cookies also work very well with fresh apricot pieces, pitted cherries, or blueberries. You can make these right away or chill the batter overnight (adding a few minutes to the baking time).

YIELD: 15 to 18 large cookies   EQUIPMENT: A stand mixer with the paddle attachment
PLAN AHEAD: Bring the goat cheese, butter, and egg to room temperature.

240 grams (1⅔ cups) unbleached all-purpose flour

3 grams (¾ teaspoon) baking powder

1.5 grams (¼ teaspoon) baking soda

1.5 grams (¼ teaspoon) fine sea salt

226 grams (8 ounces) chèvre or other fresh soft goat cheese at room-temperature

113 grams (1 stick/8 tablespoons) unsalted butter at room temperature

200 grams (1 cup) sugar

1 egg at room temperature

4 grams (1 teaspoon) vanilla extract

Grated or chopped zest of ½ lemon

1 stalk rhubarb (121 grams), sliced ¼ inch thick (1⅓ cups/about 50 pieces of fruit)

1. Heat the oven to 400°F and line a sheet pan with parchment paper. Whisk the flour, baking powder, baking soda, and salt together in a medium bowl and set aside. In the bowl of a stand mixer with the paddle attachment, cream together the goat cheese, butter, and sugar on medium speed until the sugar is nearly dissolved, about 2 minutes. Add the egg, vanilla, and lemon zest and beat on low speed until creamy, about 2 minutes.

2. Scrape down the sides of the bowl. With a flexible spatula, fold in the dry ingredients until the dough just comes together.

3. Drop large (⅛-cup) balls of dough onto the cookie sheet 3 to 4 inches apart. Press 3 or 4 pieces of rhubarb or other fruit firmly into the top of each cookie. Bake for 18 to 20 minutes or until the cookies just start to color on the top. Cool on a rack and eat within a day or two.

OSSI DI MORTI
bones of the dead

When I first tasted these, I was so desperate to know how they were made that I tracked down a recipe from a Tuscan bakery called da Lombardi in the city of Montalcino.

These are the most ethereal cookies I've ever eaten. Despite their name, and their pale, dry appearance—not to mention their misshapen resemblance to bones—they are a magical food. They are delicate and so crackly that they melt away in a flash of almond and sugar as you crunch them. They begin to dry out as soon as you pull them from the oven, as they cool, shrink, and effervesce into a chorus of snaps, crackles, and pops.

Note: This dough tends to move and settle as you work with it. Just keep patting it back into shape as you go along.

YIELD: 20 small cookies

125 grams (1 cup) whole raw almonds

75 grams (scant ¾ cup) unbleached all-purpose flour, plus flour for dusting

250 grams (1¼ cups) sugar

5 grams (1 teaspoon) baking powder

Pinch of fine sea salt

2 large egg whites

1. Heat the oven to 350°F and lightly toast the almonds on a sheet pan for 8 to 10 minutes or until a shade darker in color and just barely toasted. Set aside and let cool completely. Turn the oven down to 300°F and line two sheet pans with parchment paper.

2. Stir the flour, sugar, baking powder, and salt together in a medium bowl with a fork. Stir in the cooled almonds. Add the egg whites and stir until the dough comes together, about 1 minute. The dough will be quite soft.

3. Generously flour a piece of parchment to work on. Divide the dough in half and place one piece on the floured parchment. Dust the dough with flour and use floured hands to roll the dough into a rope about 1 inch thick and 10 inches long. Slice through the rope at 1-inch intervals. You will need to keep patting the dough back into the 1-inch rope as you go. Place the cookies 3 inches apart on a parchment-lined pan. Bake the cookies for 30 to 35 minutes or until they are just slightly browned on the top. Allow the cookies to cool completely on the pan and store in an airtight container for up to a month.

Ossi di morti.

Colpa degno.

COLPA DEGNO

flourless triple-chocolate cookies

We named these chocolate-packed rounds *colpa degno* because the term roughly translates as "worth the guilt." Created by Megan Fitzroy Phelan, currently an owner of Richmond, Virginia's lauded Longoven restaurant, and formerly a Sullivan Street pastry chef, these cookies are small and addictive and so delightful that they are well worth any remorse you might feel from eating a half dozen or so. The batter is quick, easy, and sticky and makes for cookies that are crispy, chewy, and suffused with chocolate.

YIELD: 2 dozen cookies

185 grams (1⅔ cups) confectioners' sugar

40 grams (scant ½ cup) unsweetened dark cocoa powder

2.5 grams (½ teaspoon) coarse sea salt

Whites from 2 large eggs

6 grams (1¼ teaspoons) vanilla extract

100 grams (½ cup) milk chocolate chips

100 grams (½ cup) dark chocolate chips

1. Heat the oven to 375°F and line a baking sheet with parchment paper. Whisk the powdered sugar, cocoa powder, and salt with a fork in a medium bowl to combine. Whisk together the egg whites and the vanilla with the fork in a small bowl. Make a well in the center of the dry ingredients and pour in the egg whites; stir the mixture with the fork until it just begins to come together. Add the chocolates and stir until well combined. The dough will be extremely sticky and as dark as black licorice.

2. At the bakery, we use a #60 scoop (like a small ice cream scoop) to scoop and ball these, but an ordinary 1 tablespoon measuring spoon works well too. Pack the batter into the spoon by squashing and dragging the spoon against the inside of the bowl to make sure the rounds of dough are tight and compact—if the dough is too loosely packed, the cookies tend to really spread out and separate as they bake. Place the rounds of dough on the parchment-lined cookie sheet a good 3 inches apart and bake for about 12 minutes or until the tops are glossy and set. When the cookies are done, they will be quite gooey, but they will continue to cook as they cool. Once they've cooled off enough to eat, they should be soft and chewy—if they're hard or crisp, they've baked too much. Cool the cookies on the paper, set on a wire rack, for 10 minutes. Repeat with the remaining dough. Serve these cookies the day they are made.

CIAMBELLA

ring cake

In my early days of visiting Italian village bakeries, almost every one I visited offered some version of this treat. A modest cake, *ciambella* is a bit like a classic pound cake but baked with milk and oil rather than butter. Laced with the gentle anise aroma of sambuca, the smell of a ciambella baking is to me the classic perfume of an Italian bakery.

YIELD: One 9- or 10-inch ring cake   EQUIPMENT: A 9- or 10-inch ring pan or angel food cake pan

170 grams (¾ cup) neutral-flavored oil, such as grapeseed or canola, plus oil for the pan

435 grams (3 cups) unbleached all-purpose flour

7 grams (1½ teaspoons) baking powder

4 grams (¾ teaspoon) fine sea salt

242 grams (1 cup) whole milk at room temperature

250 grams (1¼ cups) sugar

24 grams (2 tablespoons) sambuca*

4 grams (1 teaspoon) vanilla extract

165 grams (3 large) eggs at room temperature

* In a pinch, you might use this as a substitute for sambuca: steep ½ teaspoon crushed aniseeds in 2 tablespoons of vodka for 30 minutes and then strain out the seeds and use the vodka.

1. Heat the oven to 450°F. Oil a 9- or 10-inch ring pan.

2. Whisk the flour, baking powder, and salt into a small mixing bowl and set aside. Whisk the milk, sugar, sambuca, oil, and vanilla together in a large mixing bowl until the sugar dissolves. Then vigorously whisk in all three eggs.

3. Add the dry ingredients to the wet ingredients. Stir together as quickly as possible with a flexible spatula until a wet batter forms; do not overmix. Pour the batter into the ring pan and place on a sheet pan. Bake for 40 minutes or until a toothpick inserted into the cake comes out clean. Cool the cake in the pan for 5 minutes. Run a knife along the inner and outer edges of the cake and turn out onto a wire rack to cool.

VARIATION

with lemon

Omit the sambuca and replace with 2 tablespoons of limoncello. Add the zest of 1 whole lemon to the dry ingredients.

Ciambella.

Crostata di marmalata (page 216).

CROSTATA INTEGRALI
tart crust with whole wheat

On my first trip to Italy, I was a twenty-one-year-old art student. I stayed in a giant pensione in Rome run by the Vatican. The vast kitchen was run by a battalion of women whose cooking skill and style I found bewitching. It began in the morning with coffee and bread and a slice of crostata: a quick, crumbly crust pressed into a tart pan, coated with jam, and baked. Later it is one of the first treats I would make on Sullivan Street in the early days of the bakery. Here is my favorite version of crostata dough, with a bit of whole wheat for flavor. It is easy to make and easy to eat. The bit of leavening adds air and a soft, crumbly feel to the dough. It is softer than a typical tart crust and flirts with the possibility of becoming a cake.

It is important for the dough not to get too warm while you are working with it. If it begins to feel soft and sticky, pop it in the refrigerator for 10 minutes.

YIELD: One 10-inch tart crust   EQUIPMENT: A stand mixer with the paddle attachment

200 grams (1¼ cups plus 2 tablespoons) unbleached all-purpose flour

40 grams (¼ cup) whole wheat flour

2 grams (½ teaspoon) baking powder

3 grams (½ teaspoon) fine sea salt

168 grams (1½ sticks/12 tablespoons) unsalted butter at room temperature

175 grams (¾ cup plus 1 tablespoon) sugar

1 large egg

1 egg yolk

1 teaspoon finely grated lemon zest

4 grams (½ teaspoon) vanilla extract

1. Combine the flours, baking powder, and salt in a small bowl and set aside.

2. Place the butter, sugar, egg, egg yolk, lemon zest, and vanilla in the bowl of a stand mixer fitted with the paddle attachment. Mix on low speed for 5 to 7 minutes, stopping midway through to scrape down the bowl. Add the dry ingredients and gradually bring the mixer to medium speed for 1 minute.

3. Turn the dough out onto a piece of plastic wrap and pat into a ½-inch-thick disk. Cover tightly and let rest in the refrigerator for at least 1 hour and as long as 8 hours. When ready to roll out the dough, allow it to sit unwrapped for a few minutes at room temperature, until slightly pliable.

Use this crust for the Crostata di Marmalata (page 216) or the Crostata di Ricotta (page 218).

CROSTATA DI MARMALATA

quick tart with marmalade or jam

A crostata is a quick tart crust topped with a simple spread. It's the sort of welcoming treat you expect to find laid out in the kitchen, waiting as a surprise for hungry kids just out of school. It is sweet, wholesome, and satisfying, something you bake not to impress but to feed those you love.

Any jam will work for the filling. Raspberry is particularly nice, but I prefer apricot to all others. The flavors of apricot—sweet, tart, and floral—are beautiful alone and also complement the toasty flavors of the wheat. If you don't have any jam on hand, but do have a bit of fruit, I've included my recipe for an easy, quick jam.

YIELD: One 10-inch round crostata   EQUIPMENT: A 10-inch round tart pan with a removable bottom and a rolling pin

1 batch Crostata Integrali (page 215)   **250 grams (¾ cup) apricot jam (page 217 or your favorite alternative)**

1. Heat the oven to 400°F. Unwrap the dough and knead the dough on an unfloured work surface until it becomes malleable. (Do not let it become too warm or it will become unmanageably soft.) Heavily dust a work surface with flour and roll out the dough to a thickness of ¼ inch. Cut out a 12-inch circle of dough and line the tart pan. Gently press the dough into the bottom and sides of the pan. Gather the dough scraps and roll the dough into a ¼-inch-thick rope.

2. Pour the jam into the middle of the pan and use the back of a spoon to spread it evenly (thick patches will sink into the dough). It should not quite touch the edges.

3. Fashion a tic-tac-toe pattern across the top of the jam with the remaining dough. It need not be perfect—it's nice when it's pretty, but for me the lattice is pure function; when it browns deeply in the oven, I know the crostata is done. Place the tart pan on a sheet pan.

4. Bake for 30 to 35 minutes, until the top lattice is deeply browned. Cool the crostata in the pan on a wire rack for 5 minutes. Remove from the outer ring of the pan and continue to cool on the rack.

QUICK JAM

Toss 500 grams (17½ ounces) of fruit (cut into ¼- to ½-inch pieces) with 125 grams (½ cup plus 2 teaspoons) of sugar. Cook in a saucepan over high heat until it reaches a rolling boil. Carefully pass the fruit through a food mill. Return to the saucepan, bring back to a boil, and cook until thickened—usually about 10 minutes. Done!

CROSTATA DI RICOTTA

tart with ricotta, orange, and chocolate chips

This is another common version of a crostata. The crust is filled with sweet ricotta flavored with chocolate and candied orange peel. I made this often at Sullivan Street Bakery in the early days because it would always remind me of the town San Casciano dei Bagni, where I first learned to make it. The town was so tiny it felt medieval. At the time I was there, there was one bar: Bar Centrale. I went there every morning for breakfast and every afternoon for lunch. For breakfast I usually had a cappuccino and a slice of *crostata di ricotta*. When I came in at around eight or nine o'clock in the morning, the crostata was often still warm and fragrant. The owner and resident matriarch, Bruna Boni, was kind enough to show me how she made it. Here is my version, which has changed a bit over the years—just as Bruna assured me hers varied from day to day.

> **Note:** This tart will work with any ricotta, but will be even better with fresh ricotta—particularly a fresh sheep's milk ricotta.

YIELD: One 10-inch round crostata   EQUIPMENT: A 10-inch round tart pan with a removable bottom

425 grams (scant 2 cups) whole-milk ricotta

75 grams (⅓ cup) sugar

1 large egg

4 grams (1 teaspoon) dark rum

4 grams (1 teaspoon) vanilla extract

50 grams (⅓ cup) mini semisweet chocolate chips

50 grams (2 tablespoons) candied orange peel, store-bought or homemade (page 219), chopped into small pieces

1 batch Crostata Integrale (page 215)

Unbleached all-purpose flour for dusting

1. Press the ricotta through a mesh strainer or sifter to remove any lumps or whisk until smooth.

2. Heat the oven to 400°F. Whisk the ricotta, sugar, egg, rum, and vanilla together in a medium bowl until well combined. Stir in the chocolate chips and orange peel.

3. Unwrap the dough and knead the dough on an unfloured work surface until it becomes malleable. (Do not let the dough become too warm or it will become unmanageably soft.) Dust a work surface with flour and roll out the dough to a thickness of ¼ inch. Gently press the dough into the bottom and sides of the pan.

4. Pour the ricotta filling into the crust. Bake the crostata for 35 minutes or until the top has puffed up and browned nicely. Cool the crostata in the pan on a wire rack for 5 minutes. Remove from the outer ring of the pan and continue to cool on the rack—but perhaps not too much. This tart is lovely the next day, but is at its best when served while the chocolate chips inside are still melty and molten.

QUICK CANDIED ORANGE PEEL

2 large oranges
200 grams (1 cup plus 2 tablespoons) sugar

236 grams (1 cup) water
1 tablespoon light corn syrup

1. With a sharp knife, cut strips of the peel (not the white pith) from the oranges. Remove any bits of pith still on the peel. Cut the peel into narrow strips.

2. In a small saucepan, combine 1 cup of the sugar, the water, and the corn syrup and bring to a boil over high heat, stirring constantly. Add the peel and reduce the heat to low. Simmer the peel for 10 minutes or until translucent. Remove with a slotted spoon.

3. Rinse the peel under cool running water to remove the syrup. Allow the peel to dry on a wire rack. Toss the peel with the remaining 2 tablespoons sugar. Store in the refrigerator for up to 3 months.

PINOLATA

pine nut and custard pie

You'll find a version of this pastry made all over Italy, but you would be hard-pressed to find any two that are exactly alike. They are usually made with a shortbreadlike double crust filled with custard and topped with whole pine nuts. They are all a little different, they are all a little the same, and they are almost always wonderful. Here is my version.

YIELD: One 10-inch pie   EQUIPMENT: A 10-inch tart pan with a removable bottom

1 batch Crostata Integrali (page 215)
Unbleached all-purpose flour for dusting
1 batch (about 3 cups) Vanilla Pastry Cream (page 156)

70 grams (½ cup) pine nuts
1 large egg, beaten with a pinch of salt

1. Place a rack in the middle of the oven and heat to 400°F.

2. Unwrap the dough, knead until malleable, remove a third of the dough (about 150 grams), and set aside. On a floured work surface, roll out the remaining portion of the dough until it is the size of the tart pan. Transfer to the pan and use your palms to push the dough up the sides of the pan so that the edges of the dough reach the top of the pan.

3. Pour the pastry cream into the crust and use the back of a spoon to spread evenly. Reflour the work surface and roll out the remaining piece of dough into another 10-inch disk. Work quickly, before the dough softens, using as much flour as needed. Fold the dough over the rolling pin, align one edge with the edge of the tart pan, and carefully unroll it across the pan. Brush the top of the dough with the egg mixture and scatter the pine nuts across the top of the dough.

4. Place the tart pan on a sheet pan and bake for 40 to 45 minutes or until the top crust has browned evenly, the pine nuts are well toasted, and the edges of the crust are just slightly pulling away from the sides of the pan. Cool the crostata in the pan on a wire rack for 5 minutes. Remove from the outer ring of the pan and continue to cool on the rack. Serve while still warm, if possible.

Pinolata.

Focaccia fiorentina.

FOCACCIA FIORENTINA

brioche with cream

We tend to associate the word *focaccia* with savory breads, but traditionally it simply means "cake." There are many versions of a *focaccia fiorentina*—essentially a giant cream puff, cut into wedges—and this is what they call it in Florence. It is a light and delicate dessert that I particularly enjoy with fresh fruit. I have always appreciated that it is an elegant combination of two ordinary ingredients: bread and cream. The pairing is even more melodious in Italian: *pane e panna*.

> **Note:** The trick of making a beautiful brioche focaccia fiorentina is to let the brioche proof fully before baking, so that it rises beautifully in the oven and is easier to slice in half and fill.

YIELD: One 10-inch cream-filled disk of brioche   EQUIPMENT: A 10-inch cake pan

5 grams (1 teaspoon) unsalted butter for the pan

1 batch No-Knead, Naturally Leavened Brioche dough (page 107)

1 large egg

Pinch of fine sea salt

35 grams (¼ cup) chopped peeled hazelnuts or sliced almonds

35 grams (¼ cup) pine nuts

232 grams (1 cup) very cold heavy cream

Confectioners' sugar for dusting

1. Lightly butter the cake pan. Heat the oven to 400°F.

2. Turn the brioche dough into the buttered pan and gently press it out so that it fills the pan evenly. Beat the egg with a pinch of salt and brush the mixture onto the top of the dough.

3. Sprinkle all of the nuts evenly across the top of the dough. Cover the dough with a damp tea towel and allow it to proof until it is more than double its initial size. Uncover the focaccia. Bake for 20 to 25 minutes, until the top is golden brown, the nuts are just beginning to brown, and the cake is beginning to pull slightly away from the sides of the pan.

4. Remove from the oven, allow to cool for 5 minutes in the pan, and then remove from the pan and allow to cool completely on a wire rack.

5. Whip the cream in a large bowl until stiff peaks form. Use a long serrated knife to cut through the middle of the cake as if you were making a layer cake. Gently remove the top, pour the whipped cream into the middle of the focaccia, and spread evenly, leaving a 1-inch border around the focaccia. Replace the top, dust with confectioners' sugar, and serve *immediately.*

Traditional panettone.

PANETTONE

a grand bread

(This recipe requires the stiff starter, or biga, on page 51, and can be "kneaded" in a stand mixer.)

A panettone is the apotheosis of natural leavening.

This bread is so sweet it could almost be a cake—but there was never a cake this silky and soft and stratospherically built. The scaffolding of the airiest, lightest, fluffiest rustic bread is directed here to a sweet bread, to create a confection so marvelous it is traditionally eaten once a year, to celebrate the Christmas holidays. The amount of butter, eggs, sugar, rum-soaked raisins, and cubes of candied citron mixed into the dough means that, like the pyramids of Egypt, this bread will take time to rise, but will, eventually, reach astounding heights.

Traditionally a panettone is baked in a 9-inch paper panettone mold (often available online—look for a paper baking mold that is 9 inches across on the bottom and 7 inches high), but an easy substitute is a simple round glass baking dish. The refrigerator-to-oven type sold in supermarkets with a plastic lid is perfect. Extend their height with a double lining of parchment paper that is cut long enough to stick up 7 or 8 inches into the air. The panettone will inflate like a hot-air balloon in the oven, and it will be extremely fragile when it has finished baking. To prevent it from collapsing as it cools, a panettone is traditionally hung upside down to dry, or "cure." So before you begin your own panettone, make sure you have metal or sturdy wood skewers and room somewhere in your home to cure the panettone for a few hours after it comes out of the oven.

The panettone is part of the currency of Italian life—it is a popular thing to give another family to celebrate Christmas and the New Year. It is meant to be eaten with prosecco or champagne a few hours before or after a meal or even for breakfast the morning after. Often families will put it near the radiator or in front of the fireplace so that it can warm gently before it's eaten. (If you lack a crackling fire, 30 seconds in a microwave achieves a similar effect.)

(CONTINUES)

Note on the dough: This highly enriched dough will at first seem extremely wet and elastic when it's mixed—and that's being optimistic. Uncharitable observers of this dough might call it a soup. It will be so sticky, stretchy, and stringy—really just plain messy—that you may think nothing good could possibly come of it. But as it leavens—and this will take a long time thanks to all the extra nutrients packed in here—it will double and even quadruple its initial volume before it is ready to shape. As it grows, the dough will inflate with gas, and its texture will soften and lighten.

YIELD: One 8- or 9-inch-tall, 7-inch-wide panettone
EQUIPMENT: A stand mixer fitted with the pastry paddle, one 9-inch paper panettone mold or 7-inch round flat-bottomed baking dish such as a 1.75-quart Pyrex or ceramic soufflé dish, and two 12-inch long metal skewers

80 grams (½ cup) raisins, soaked in ¼ cup very hot water for 20 minutes

100 grams (½ heaping cup) cubed candied citron* or Quick Candied Orange Peel (page 219)

113 grams (1 stick/8 tablespoons) unsalted butter, plus 14 grams (1 tablespoon) for the fruit and 14 grams (1 tablespoon) cold for baking, shaped into a square pat

* Citron is the grandparent of all modern citrus. It is mostly peel and pith, with a small sour fruit in the center. The skin is candied. I prefer using whole citron from Sicily because the texture is firm and the flavor is less sweet, with a certain brightness to it. I often find it in Italian markets. You can also use candied dried fruit in syrup; rinse the syrup off in running water and allow the fruit to dry before using.

300 grams (2 cups) unbleached all-purpose flour, plus flour for dusting

4 grams (½ teaspoon) fine sea salt

125 grams (½ cup plus 2 tablespoons) water

115 grams (½ cup plus 2 teaspoons) sugar

2 large eggs

5 grams (1 teaspoon) honey

4 grams (1 teaspoon) vanilla extract

Zest of ½ lemon (7 grams), finely chopped or grated

100 grams biga (page 51)

1. Stir the flour and salt together in a small bowl and set aside. In a small saucepan, melt 1 stick plus 1 tablespoon of the butter. Drain but do not dry the raisins. In a small bowl, combine the raisins and citron with 1 tablespoon of the melted butter and set aside.

2. Add the water to the rest of the melted butter in the saucepan and stir to combine. Heat the water and butter to 100°F, just above body temperature. Transfer the warm water and butter mixture to the bowl of a stand mixer fitted with a pastry paddle.

3. Add the sugar and mix on low speed until the sugar is dissolved. Mix in the eggs, honey, vanilla, and lemon zest on low speed until emulsified. Stop the mixer, add the biga, and continue to mix on low until it is mostly broken up. Add the flour and salt and mix for 2 or 3 minutes or until all the ingredients come together. Increase the speed to high and mix for 10 to 15 agonizingly long minutes, until the dough is sticky, bouncy, and webby—it will form long strings and strands—and pulls away from the sides of the bowl. You may hear your mixer begin to strain as the dough becomes clumped around the paddle; the dough may even ball up around the paddle. Stop the mixer when this happens; the dough is ready. Lower the mixing bowl and use a plastic dough scraper or rubber spatula to remove the dough from the paddle. Lift the bowl back up and pour the raisins and citron on the top of the dough.

4. Mix on low speed for 5 seconds. Stop the mixer and scrape the dough from the paddle. Mix for another 5 seconds on low speed. Stop the mixer, scrape the dough off the paddle, and repeat one or two times or until the raisins and citron are evenly distributed throughout the dough. This is a delicate operation; you want to incorporate the raisins and citron into the dough but also want to ensure that they are not mashed.

5. If you won't need your mixing bowl for a few days, you could leave the dough in it and cover it loosely. Otherwise, transfer the dough to a 5-quart mixing bowl or other large container, cover, and allow to ferment. It will quadruple in size and is likely to reach the top of the bowl. Depending on the temperature in your kitchen and outside, it could take 15 to 48 hours. (The optimal temperature is 70°F; if your house is much hotter or cooler than that, try to find a small space near that temperature.) The texture will become extremely stringy and elastic, and poking into it with a finger will reveal a weblike structure. It will smell like vanilla and—thanks to the sugar-enhanced fermentation—alcohol.

6. Dust flour around the edges of the dough. Use a dough scraper or rubber spatula to gently get under the dough and scrape it away from the sides and bottom of the bowl. Turn the dough out onto a floured work surface and gently fold the corners of the dough into the center to make a ball. With floured hands, gently pick up and turn the dough over so the seam is down. Gently shape the dough into a round by tucking the sides down and under—taking extra care not to stretch the dough too much; if the dough has too much tension, the raisins and citron will begin to pop out from the dough (and subsequently burn as they cook). Be as careful as you can to avoid working flour into the dough—you want the flour there only to prevent the dough from sticking and tearing.

(CONTINUES)

Panettone, in Pictures

1 Leave the dough in the mixing bowl or transfer to a large container.

2 The dough will rise slowly but dramatically.

3 When quadrupled in size, shape quickly into a round and transfer to a mold placed on a sheet pan.

4 Wait until the dough rises to just under the top of the mold.

5 Score and top with butter, then transfer to the oven.

6 Ensure there is a place to hang the panettone upside down.

7 When completely cool, store or serve the panettone.

8 The finished texture will be soft and airy, nearly a cake.

7. Gently lower the dough seam side down into a panettone mold sitting on a sheet pan. Cover the mold with a damp towel and allow to proof on the sheet pan until just shy of the top edge of the mold. It will take 3 to 7 hours.

8. Heat the oven to 350°F. Have a cold tablespoon-sized pat of butter on hand. Use a very sharp serrated knife to gently score the surface of the dough with a cross, from edge to edge, just barely cracking the surface of the dough. Place the tablespoon of cold butter in the center of the cross. (The butter helps the top of the dough stay moist and open up into triangles.) Put the panettone—still on the sheet pan, so that you don't have to touch the mold and risk deflating the panettone—into the oven. Bake for about 55 minutes or until the outside of the panettone is beautifully browned and golden.

9. Immediately drive two long skewers through the paper mold—about ½ inch or less from the bottom of the mold. Very carefully pick up the panettone and hang it upside down by the skewers until it has cooled completely. If the panettone does not cool upside down, it will collapse. A panettone will last for several weeks to a month if kept in a sealed container, although it is rare that even a slice will last the space of an hour.

VARIATION

CHOCOLATE CHERRY PANETTONE

Substitute dried sour cherries for the raisins, dark chocolate for the citron, and almond oil for the vanilla. Omit the lemon zest.

RESOURCES

Biga: If you don't want to make your own, order a small piece of Sullivan Street Bakery's biga at sullivanstreetbakery.com.

Candied citron and orange peel: If you cannot find these locally, marketfoodhall.com sells beautiful versions of these. The large pieces (half a citron or slices of orange) tend to have the cleanest flavors, although they can be quite pricey.

Flour: Unbleached all-purpose flour from the grocery store is suitable for every recipe in the book that calls for white flour. I often like to bake with the regional flours available in the regions of the country where they are grown. Often these flours are not distributed nationally. Here are a few suppliers of unique flours if you would like to try a specialty flour and cannot find one near you.

Central Milling   centralmilling.com
Eden Foods flours   edenfoods.com
Arrowhead Mills   arrowheadmills.com

Kimchi: Hawthorne Valley Farm's gorgeous kimchi (referenced in the Chicken, Avocado, and Kimchi Sandwiches recipe on page 185) is available online through farmtopeople.com. Many grocery stores now stock the more traditional varieties of kimchi; look for them in the refrigerated section near the pickles.

Panettone molds: These paper molds are a bit like giant cupcake liners and are readily available from national retailers such as Sur La Table. Look for the largest size made—usually about 7 inches in diameter.

Pots: Lodge cast-iron pots come in a variety of sizes and shapes, work well for baking bread, and are useful for nearly everything else on the stovetop as well. Staub pots are bit more of an investment but are lined with an enamel finish and are durable, beautiful, and versatile—these are my favorite. Emile Henry's ceramic bread cloches (bell-shaped pots with a large lid and flat base) are easy to use and the perfect solution if you want a dedicated bread-baking vessel.

ACKNOWLEDGMENTS

None of this would have ever happened the way it did were it not for Joe Allen, who was clever or crazy enough to open a business with me. Thank you for showing a wild kid the way. I am also deeply grateful to and proud of all the employees of Sullivan Street Bakery now and over the years. You make, pack, and deliver such beautiful bread, and clean up such tremendous messes. You have seen the bakery through actual and metaphorical hurricanes, have weathered water shutdowns and oven breakdowns, near-daily vehicle repair, and constant tinkering to keep the baking schedule on track through hot summers, freezing winters, and those special times when we forget to put leavening in the dough. When I started the bakery, I felt like a one-man show. Nothing could be further from the case now, and I am humbled by the work of all the people whose talent, dedication, ingenuity, and long hours keep the business running. Thank you, all.

I would never have completed this book without the assistance of Martha Hall Foose, who tested these recipes and made many a wise suggestion. I am also obliged to a number of others who did experiments, tried recipes, or read drafts along the way: Kathy Diehl, Laura Kinsey Dolph, Stanley Ginsberg, Mary Joseph, Tanya Joseph, Kathy Hughes Lahey, Carol Mason, Joji Pattam, Jeremy Shapiro, and Saiko Shinamura. Ian Lowe kindly extended his expertise in the arts of fermentation and baking all the way from Tasmania to fill in the gaps in my own knowledge.

Many others contributed cooking, baking, and prep hours over the last few years: Mark Barbire, Megan Fitzroy Phelan, and Ashley Whitmore made amazing food, tested recipes, and contributed some creations of their own, and Maria Allauca and Barbara Tylko helped with innumerable recipes and experiments.

Emily Isaac and Madelyn Osten mixed endless doughs to make our photo shoot possible, and light master Squire Fox and his photography team of Nan Whitney, Fred Lam, and Diana Perez captured remarkably serene photos of my whirlwind baking. I thank the team at Norton—especially Nathaniel Dennett, Ingsu Liu, Susan Sanfrey, and Anna Oler—for their hard work and for being so terrific to work with. Janis Donnaud, my agent, pushed this idea into creation, and my editor, Maria Guarnaschelli, fought tooth and nail to make this a better book. I am grateful for her tenacity and guidance. Special thanks as well to my forbearing assistant, right hand, and sidekick, Peter Hoffman, who so gracefully wears a variety of hats.

Despite such excellent collaboration, errors and flaws undoubtedly remain and these ought to be considered mine alone.

INDEX

Note: Page numbers in *italics* refer to illustrations.